The boy she fell in love with was gone...

"Do you know," Jon's voice drawled, "you've grown more beautiful than I would ever have believed possible?"

Kathryn could think of no reply. He was obviously baiting her, and now he smiled maliciously.

"And it's all going to be wasted on an old man. Tell me, do you love him as passionately as you once loved me?"

As she opened her mouth to speak, he held up his hand. "No, on second thought, don't tell me. I was a fool. I should have known better than to let you go. I could have enjoyed your... company a little longer. After all, one can always—" he paused and his gaze wandered over her ."—enjoy a beautiful woman, even though love isn't there to lend its sweetness and spice."

LILIAN PEAKE

---

man of granite

Harlequin Books

TORONTO • LONDON • LOS ANGELES • AMSTERDAM
SYDNEY • HAMBURG • PARIS • STOCKHOLM • ATHENS • TOKYO

Harlequin Presents edition published October 1975
ISBN 0-373-10113-9

Second printing October 1977
Third printing June 1978
Fourth printing March 1980
Fifth printing February 1981
Sixth printing April 1981
Seventh printing July 1981

Original hardcover edition published in 1971
by Mills & Boon Limited

CHAPTER I

GEOFF came whistling down the stairs and pushed open the door into his sister's living-room.

'Isn't that kettle boiling yet?'

'Tea's made,' Kathryn called from the kitchen. 'Just bringing it in.'

Her brother sat down and inspected his hands. 'I've got most of the paint off. Ah, thanks,' he took a cup of tea from the tray, 'just what I needed.' He helped himself liberally to sugar. 'Good thing the room's not in use. It's taken me such a time. There are too many spare rooms in this house, and they all need redecorating.'

Kathryn sympathised, 'If I weren't going out, I'd give you a hand.'

'Got a date with the Old Boy?' His tone became prim and mincing. 'Or should I call it an appointment with Mr. Rutland?'

Kathryn winced. 'Don't call Francis the Old Boy, Geoff.'

'Why not? I'm not the only member of staff who does. All college principals have nicknames and he's had his for years, you know that.'

'I know, but——'

'But it upsets you just the same, reminds you of his age, doesn't it? Look, Kath, I know we've hammered all this out before, but I wonder if you really know what you're doing. You are nearly twenty-seven, but he, dear sister, is fifty-two, a whole twenty-five years your senior. Can't you think again? Is it wise to marry a man old enough to be your father?'

Kathryn twisted the brilliant diamond around her engagement finger. 'You've said that till I'm tired of hearing it, Geoff, but it's no use. It's security I want now, not passionate love. I had that nearly ten years ago, and look where it landed me—in the divorce court by the time I was twenty-one.'

'That was your own stupid fault. You should have gone to America with Jon. After all, you were his wife. I know you were

5

only seventeen, a mere kid, but your place was beside him. Even Gran thought you'd made a terrible mistake.'

'But you know very well why I stayed behind. I felt I couldn't leave Gran after all she had done for us when Mother and Dad died. And you were only fifteen, remember. You had years of study in front of you before you got all your engineering qualifications. Don't forget, too, I was the only one bringing money into the family apart from the lodgers' rents.' She frowned. 'Anyway, I'm still convinced Jon wanted to be free of me.'

'Well, as for writing and telling him you'd found someone else and would be divorcing him for desertion, when all the time you were crazily in love with him . . .' He shook his head sadly.

Kathryn stared reflectively into the fireplace. 'And Jon believed me, wrote and told me if I wanted my freedom, I could have it, because he certainly didn't want to keep an unfaithful wife tied to him. Said he was only twenty-two, and would, like me, enjoy being released from the shackles of matrimony.' She sighed. 'So ended a beautiful marriage, all six wonderful months of it. But that was all a very long time ago.'

Geoff persisted. 'If you're determined to carry on with this engagement, Kath, make quite sure it's what you really want, because I'd hate to see you messing up your life a second time. You can't love the Old Boy, be honest.'

'I'm fond of Francis,' she said primly.

Her brother jerked his shoulders with irritation. 'Fond? Ugh, fond!' He walked out, saying, 'Thanks for the tea. I'm going to Helen's this evening. Enjoy your outing, *if* you can. And don't let the Old Boy get too affectionate. Or is he so old he's even beyond that?'

He laughed loudly as he stamped up the thinly carpeted stairs, and heard his sister slam the door behind him.

Kathryn had shared the rambling Victorian house with her brother since their grandmother had died eighteen months ago. Once they had occupied it as a family, but now there were just the two of them. When their parents had been killed twelve years before in a road accident, their grandmother had risen magnificently to the occasion.

'I'm all you've got now,' she told them. 'I'm going to give you

6

a good education even if I have to take in lodgers to bring in some money.' And that was what she did.

When Kathryn had left school, she had enrolled as a student in secretarial subjects at the large technical college in the town. She passed all her examinations and got a job as a shorthand-typist in a local solicitor's office. There she met another new girl called Margery, who said she was determined to find Kathryn a boy-friend.

'You'd better come to tea and meet my brother. His name's Jon. He's just left university and he's training to be a teacher. He's got a weakness for blondes, so he's sure to like you. His last girl-friend went off with someone else.'

A few days later, she met Margery's handsome and clever brother. They fell so much in love they could hardly bear to be apart. So Gran suggested the obvious—why didn't they get married? There was room for Jon in the house, and with his grant and Kathryn's salary, and no rent to pay, they would have no financial troubles.

So they were married. Kathryn changed her job and became a typist in the general office of the technical college where she had studied. One summer evening, Jon had dropped his bombshell. He told his wife that he had been offered the chance of a year's post-graduate research in the United States. Kathryn knew he was highly gifted and rejoiced in such an opportunity for him. She was determined not to hold him back.

'You must come with me, Kathy,' he had told her. 'Life wouldn't be worth living without you.'

But she had refused, and he had been quite unable to make her change her mind. She told him she could not leave her grandmother alone to cope with her brother, who was by then a demanding teenager. So, confident in the binding strength of their love, she told him,

'Go without me, Jon, and come home to me when you've finished your studies. It's only for a year, after all.'

He had taken her in his arms. 'Twelve months, fifty-two weeks, the number gets bigger the more you think about it. If you start counting the days, it's even worse, darling. Come with me. I don't want to leave you behind.'

But she had been adamant.

She had told no one of the agony of those lonely months without her beloved husband. When the year had nearly passed,

7

he wrote and told her that he had decided to accept the offer of yet another year's research. His decision came as a terrible shock to her and it seemed clear that he was plainly regretting an impetuous marriage to a young wife so early in his career. She realised then that she would have to let him go for ever.

A heavy knock on the front door startled Kathryn back to the present. Francis had called to pick her up. Geoff was nowhere to be seen. He made no secret of the dislike he felt for his prospective brother-in-law.

'Bad enough to have him as boss at work,' he would grumble, 'without having him invade your home.'

The evening Kathryn and Francis spent at the elegant home of their mutual friends, the Creswells, was pleasant enough. Kathryn had recognised early that she would have to accustom herself to the company of the older generation. George Creswell, fiftyish, balding, pedantic in the way that lawyers often are, was a contemporary of Francis, and had known Kathryn for many years.

He had dealt with her parents' affairs after their deaths, had helped Kathryn and her brother when their grandmother had died, and had acted for Kathryn in securing her divorce from her husband. He and his wife had been pleased when their manoeuvrings had brought together their old friend Francis Rutland, who was a widower, and their young acquaintance, Kathryn Swale, who, in their opinion, had been somewhat harshly treated by fate.

Francis drove her home from the Creswells'.

'What did you think of that house they told us about, my dear? Do you like the idea of buying a completely new one? I must say I should rather like it.'

'So would I, Francis, and since it's only half-built, I suppose we could look it over any time. Did they have any idea how long it would take to finish?'

'George mentioned six months at least. It's on a new estate at the other end of the town, in rural surroundings. If this couple who are trying to raise a mortgage on it are unsuccessful, then I think we should seriously consider it. The price is right, and if necessary we could at this stage make basic alterations to the design.'

She closed her eyes in the darkness of the car and wondered

idly if Mrs. Creswell knew about her marriage to Jon ten years ago, and her subsequent divorce. It worried her just a little because she had not yet told her fiancé about it, allowing him instead to think of her as a young widow. Mrs. Creswell was such a chatterbox and talked so unguardedly that Kathryn felt it could not be long before her fiancé came across the truth by way of Mrs. Creswell's prattle. To forestall this possibility she knew she would soon have to tell him herself.

Francis was saying, 'The new head of the science department takes up his duties tomorrow, my dear. You will arrive early to greet him, won't you, and put him at his ease? As his secretary, you will be able to give him an extra bit of help at first.'

'Of course, Francis. By the way, I know his name, but that's all. What's he like? I was off work with a cold the day he was appointed. I've asked other people, but they're as much in the dark about him as I am.'

'Well, he's a Ph.D., and he's coming from industry, but trained for teaching some years ago, although he has never put theory into practice until now. Got excellent qualifications and references, clever chap, studied abroad for a time. He's a good deal younger than his predecessor, Mr. Smithers. Hope you get on well with him.'

'So do I.' The words reverberated agitatedly in her brain. The car came to a standstill at a road junction and she stared at the red signal of the traffic lights, strangely fascinated by its brilliance against the background of the darkness.

'Wright is his name,' she whispered to herself. 'He's a Ph.D., so he'll be Doctor Wright. One day, when I know him better, I'll tell him, "We share a surname, Dr. Wright. My married name is—was—Wright. Isn't it odd that we should be working together?" The traffic lights changed and the forward movement of the car jerked her back, then forwards. She sat up. 'It couldn't be, could it? It couldn't be Jon? Studied abroad, Francis said. Clever chap. Trained for teaching years ago.' She sank back. Wright was a common name. There was a lecturer on the staff already, name of Wright, in the art department. No, it couldn't be Jon. Francis opened the car door.

'Goodnight now, my dear.' He gave her a chaste peck on the cheek.

'Goodnight, Francis.' As she waved and watched him drive away, she felt glad he was an undemonstrative person, and that he never touched her except for a gentle kiss such as he had just given her.

'Although we've been engaged for nearly two months,' she reflected, as she opened the front door, 'we've never even held hands. I don't think I could stand it if he wanted more of me than that. I could never feel for any other man what I felt for Jon.'

She pushed firmly into the alcoves of her mind the niggling thoughts which did their best to remind her that marriage and engagements were two very different things, and that any man, married to an attractive young woman, would demand far more than a chaste kiss now and then.

Kathryn left the house especially early next morning. She got off the bus and walked down the long drive towards the technical college, the gravel crunching underfoot, and her eyes scanned the entrance foyer through the giant panes of glass which the architects had thought fit to install in place of solid bricks and mortar.

She looked at the clock in the entrance foyer and decided it was time she made for her office and prepared herself to meet the newcomer. As she climbed the flight of stairs to the first floor, she wondered once again what he was like. 'It couldn't be Jon,' she assured herself yet again. 'Coincidences like that just don't happen.'

She opened her office door and removed her coat, hearing the murmur of voices from the head of department's room. She renewed her make-up and tidied her hair, then sat at her typewriter, only to rise immediately as the inner door from the head's room opened and two men came in. One was Fred Welford, head of the engineering department. The other was the new member of staff. Kathryn stared at the handsome face which seemed to swim momentarily in front of her eyes, and her hand flew to her throat. She wished she could grasp her heart in her hand to stop its mad, throbbing beat.

'Miss Swale, meet Dr. Wright, head of the science department—in other words, your new boss.'

Fred Welford was introducing them with a flourish. 'Dr. Wright, your own personal secretary, Miss Kathryn Swale. Count yourself lucky you've got her. She's the best secretary on the staff.'

Kathryn saw him standing there, tall, lean, his hair thick and brown, his eyes deeply probing, and could scarcely breathe. 'It is, it *is* Jon,' she thought. She clasped her hands to stop them trembling. The years have hardly touched him.

Kathryn's gaze locked with his and each in silent astonishment questioned the other. There came a striving on the part of both to bridge the gaping chasm which the years apart had opened up between them. Kathryn's tremulous smile reached out to him in incredulous greeting and, unguarded as he momentarily was by sheer disbelief that they had been brought together again, his features came alive in response. But the fire so spontaneously kindled was immediately and with complete finality extinguished by the poison of bitter memories.

His eyes became like two rooms plunged into sudden darkness, and cynicism groped its twisted way out of them to snatch the half-formed words of greeting from Kathryn's lips. As she looked at him, she was conscious of a force within him which had been roughened and gnarled by something more powerful than the process of maturity, and she drew back in dismay at the harshness of his gaze.

His hand, as it met hers briefly, was cold, and he removed it as if he could hardly bear the contact.

'Miss Swale?' he asked, his eyebrows quivering upwards the merest fraction. '*Miss* Swale?'

Kathryn nodded dumbly and Fred Welford misunderstanding, laughed heartily. 'Yes, old boy, as yet, Miss Swale. Hard to believe, isn't it? But not for long, as you can see from the lady's third finger, left hand. She is, as they say, bespoke—to the principal, no less. So keep your eyes off, boy. She's yours for a while, but not more than a few months, eh, Miss Swale? Isn't that so, Miss Swale?'

Kathryn had by now recovered some of her usual composure.

'A good few months yet, Mr. Welford. So Dr. Wright can rest assured that I shall see him well settled in before I—desert him.'

'Well, old chap, I'll leave you to your secretary's tender mercies.' He put up his hand and whispered loudly behind it, 'Sooner me than you, I can tell you.' The door closed behind him, cutting off his hearty laughter.

The silence between them had to be broken.

Kathryn said, hesitantly, 'I'm—I'm sorry this had to happen,

11

but unfortunately there's nothing, nothing at all we can do about it, is there?'

His eyes narrowed. 'No? Is there not? We shall have to see, won't we?'

As he turned away, she spoke again. 'Is there anything I can do to help you?'

He stood for a moment at the communicating door between his room and her office. 'If I want you, I shall call you.' The door slammed behind him.

Fighting the tears which came from her very depths, she sank into her chair and held her head. What cruel twist of fate had made this happen? How could they work together if his attitude was to be so unforgiving and so uncompromising? What had the years done to him? There never was before that hardness of stone in his eyes, that touch of granite about his whole person.

She tried to pull herself together, while her self-control gave first aid to her shattered emotions. Automatically, she sorted through the post, selecting a handful of letters which she could deal with herself, without troubling the new head of department. Having collected the information necessary to answer them, she typed suitable replies. Her mind was functioning with machine-like precision, without any conscious effort. She felt she was playing a part in a terrible nightmare.

As she worked, the same monotonous phrases chased each other round her brain. What could she do about it, what would he do about it?

With the typewritten letters in her hand, she tapped on his door and entered.

His expression hardened. 'Yes, what do you want?'

She approached his desk. 'I hope you don't object, but I've picked out a few letters from your post and answered them myself. Would you mind signing them, please?'

'You've *what*?' She reeled backwards under the impact of his anger. 'Answered some of my letters without first allowing me to read them, and without even asking my permission? Is this a habit of yours?'

'I'm—I'm sorry.' She was aghast at his tone. 'I only did it to help you. I always did it for your predecessor, Mr. Smithers.'

'Look, Miss Swale.' He leaned back in his chair. 'Let's get this straight from the start. I'm a new man here, with new ideas.

What was all right for my predecessor almost certainly won't be right for me. So in future, since I, as head of department, must take ultimate responsibility, I wish to be consulted before you take anything on your own shoulders. Initiative is a fine thing in the right place and the right person. In my opinion, the right person to exercise initiative is not the secretary, but the boss. Understand?'

Kathryn took a grip on herself, controlled her shaking hands. 'Yes, Dr.—Dr. Wright.'

He slapped the top of his desk irritably. 'Put the letters there. I'll vet them, and if necessary you'll have to type them again. If not, all right, this time I'll sign them. Now leave me in peace. I've got one hell of a problem on my hands, I'm sure you must agree.'

She closed the door between them and sank, white-faced and unbelieving, on to her chair. For half an hour she stared into space, reviewing the whole impossible situation. Her mind perspired as she struggled to find a solution. She couldn't resign from her job, because she needed the money. There was little likelihood that Francis would bring forward their wedding date, because he insisted on their making a fresh start in a new house. Jon could not get rid of her, because she was senior to all the other secretaries, and there would be too much raising of eyebrows and awkward questions asked if he tried to effect a change.

Fred Welford put his head round the door. 'Just taking your boss on a grand tour of the college, Kathryn. Won't keep him any longer than I need. How're you getting on with him? Got him where you want him yet? It doesn't take most secretaries long to get their bosses in that state, let alone a darned attractive one like you!' The sound of something heavy crashing on to the desk top in the other room made him withdraw his head.

'Well, that's one use for a paperweight, to terminate a frivolous conversation,' thought Kathryn ruefully. 'I'd better be careful it doesn't come flying in my direction some time.'

By the time she arrived home, she was emotionally exhausted, and tried to revive her flagging spirits with a cup of tea. She prepared the evening meal, then started packing a case for Geoff, who was off to London the next morning for a two-day engineering course.

The front door opened, and Kathryn called, 'Come in here,

13

Geoff, before you go upstairs, will you? I want to talk to you.'

'Hallo,' he greeted her, 'what's up?' Then he saw her face. '*Is* there anything wrong, Kath?'

She answered him slowly, having some difficulty in getting the words out. Her brain seemed numb, and in a state of shock. 'Have you met the new head of the science department today?'

'Your new boss? Can't say I have. Why? I heard he was around this afternoon, but I was lecturing, so I missed him.'

'Do you know his name?'

'Name? Yes, they told me. It's something like Wright. I remembered it for obvious reasons, connecting it with your married name. But there are dozens of Wrights around, nothing to do with you.'

'His name,' still she spoke slowly, staring at him, 'is Dr. Wright, Dr. Jon Wright.'

'Is that so? An even greater coincid——' He broke off and stared back at her. '*Jon* Wright? Not, surely, not your ex-husband?'

She nodded and sat on the arm of the chair to steady herself. Geoff's face glowed. 'Not old Jon, after all these years? Well, I'm blessed! I'll look him up tomorrow, first thing. Oh darn, I can't. There's this course I'm going on. Give him my warmest regards, will you? I bet you were delighted to see him. Tell me, what was the reunion like? Or is it a secret?'

He saw with disbelief the tears which flooded into her eyes. 'Hey, what's up? Has he got remarried, or something?'

She shook her head helplessly. That possibility had not occurred to her. 'Geoff, he hates me. He's mad about me being his secretary. He's obviously never forgiven me, and it seems as though he never will. He's going to try to get me moved.'

'But he can't do that. You're the most senior typist there, that's why you've got that job, because it's the largest department.'

'Geoff, you and I know that, but he doesn't. It's plain by his venomous attitude towards me he'll move heaven and earth to get rid of me.'

'Oh, blast this course. I'll have to speak to him about it as soon as I get back.'

'It's no good. It'll be too late by then.'

As her brother went upstairs, she called to him, 'Is Helen coming after tea?'

'No. She's taking a shorthand class tonight. By the time she gets away from the students, it'll be too late. You know they all hang round the teacher afterwards, asking advice and so on.'

'We'll just have a quiet evening then, you working, me brooding!' She smiled sadly.

'You poor kid.' He really did sound upset. 'I wish I could do something to help you, Kath. You've been good to me, I'd like to repay some of it.'

'Thanks, Geoff, for the kind thought, anyway.'

Next morning, Kathryn got up early and saw Geoff off to London. She washed the breakfast dishes, then caught the bus to work.

Jon was there before her. She was running a comb through her hair and powdering her nose when she heard the door of his office open. He waited for a tense moment while she guiltily put her belongings into her handbag, then he spoke.

'Come into my room, please,' adding sarcastically, 'when you can spare the time, of course.'

Her heart sank. So he had started already. She removed the cover from her typewriter, took up her pencil and notepad, tried to still the suffocating thudding of her heart and went in to him.

He saw her shorthand pad. 'Oh, put that away, you won't need that yet. Sit down. I have something to say to you.'

She sank on to the chair in front of his desk, and looked up at him. He stood beside the chair, hands in pockets. His face was expressionless, and he paused a moment before speaking.

'You probably know what I'm going to say. Somehow we've got to become reconciled to the situation in which we find ourselves, obviously through no fault of our own. I've been awake half the night trying to think of a solution. I've come to these conclusions.'

He picked up a ruler, put it down, straightened his blotter. Suddenly he transferred his gaze to her face. She watched him, frightened almost of what he was going to say.

'Let me tell you at the outset. If I had known who my personal secretary was going to be, I would have turned the job down without any hesitation. However, that is past. It did occur to me that I could ask for a change of secretary——'

Kathryn opened her mouth to speak, but he held up his

hands. 'Excuse me, but I'm doing the talking now. I am aware that if I were to ask for other secretarial help, it would cause comment and speculation. I would also no doubt be told I was mad to want a change,' his smile was derisive, 'because I'm sick and tired of being told how lucky,' his tone made the word abusive, 'I am to have you. Needless to say, I have my own views on that. However, I decided that I shall perforce have to keep you as my secretary, with the following proviso:

'Since our—relationship nearly ten years ago was of such short duration, lasting in fact about as long as a so-called love affair; since it was so long ago we are now as strangers, I suggest—no, I insist—that we behave towards each other as though we had never met before, and as though we were not even as close as friends in the distant past. In other words, now that we are nearly ten years older, we are really two entirely different people, and I'm afraid my attitude to you will be even less friendly than a man usually is towards his secretary, because the bitter feelings I have where you are concerned will allow me to be nothing else.'

He waited, giving her a chance to reply, but she could not even think coherently, let alone speak. So he continued, 'The thought has just occurred to me that you probably had a much deeper, more lasting association with the other man than you had with me.'

She opened her mouth to cry out in agony, 'There never was another man,' but he silenced her.

'No, don't tell me how long your liaison lasted. I don't want to hear the sordid details of your past.'

He was plainly determined not to listen to anything she had to say in her own defence.

She whispered from a parched throat, 'Is that all?'

'No, that is not all. I must have your solemn promise that neither you nor your brother who, I hear, is on the staff of this college, will say a word to anyone of our past relationship.'

She answered with quiet dignity, 'You have my word that I shall be silent on the whole subject, and I'm sure Geoff will give his assurance to be likewise.'

'Thank you. I simply don't want my present life to be hampered and invaded by my past—mistakes. You have your life to live, I have mine. There will be no connection between the two.'

16

She began to rise, but he motioned to her to keep her seat.

'I still have not finished.' His tone rebuked her. 'Our positions are even more complicated by the fact that you are, I understand, engaged to be married to the principal. I wish to make it quite clear that whatever I may say about him, his work or his ideas, must not be passed on to him by you. As my secretary, you will be in receipt of my confidences, as any other person in your position would be. I must feel free to express my opinion of anyone, including your—your fiancé,' he plainly did not like the sound of the word, 'without wondering how much will be conveyed back to him.'

Kathryn sprang up angrily.

'So, in addition to everything else that you accuse me of, you now insinuate that I'm a sneak!'

Her blue eyes blazed into his, she breathed quickly and struggled to control the shaking of her fingers as they grasped the notepad in her hands.

A faint smile touched his mouth as he waited for her to calm down. 'I see by your rather frenzied reaction to my words that you've at last got the message.'

'Now have you finished with me?'

He lowered himself in to his swivel chair and swung to and fro, considering her. He saw her fair hair curling softly round her flushed face. He contemplated her petite but shapely figure beneath her attractive blue wool dress; he looked at her curving red lips and her sky-blue eyes clouded with indignant tears. Then he smiled, and his words were biting and contemptuous. 'Finished with you? I can answer that unequivocally and without any hesitation whatsoever. Yes, absolutely finished with you. Thanks.

Their eyes clashed like cymbals being struck together. She turned away and slammed his door behind her, knowing with maddening certainty that it would only bring a smile of triumph to his lips.

Struggling to control her tears, Kathryn put down her notepad and stared out of the window. She saw the newly completed art and printing block, towering eight storeys high, its multiplicity of windows, some open, some shut, reflecting like facets of a diamond the pale January sunshine. She looked across the paved way to domestic science and commerce

17

block, where Geoff's girl-friend, Helen Brown, was working The college playing fields were a soothing expanse of green beyond the buildings and as she absent-mindedly watched a group of students playing football, she looked back over the years and realised how entangled her life had been with the college since her teens. Geoff's life, too, was tied up with the place. He had studied there, and after qualifying had been accepted on to the lecturing staff.

Now she was engaged to the principal, and was secretary to a man she had passionately loved, but who had now become an impossible tyrant and who seemed to hate the very air she breathed. The man she had loved—she knew with sudden dismay that her loving had not ended. It seemed, instead, to have increased with the years, and he had only to lift his little finger and she would go running to him without reserve.

She turned quickly as the door from the corridor opened.

'Hallo there.' Helen cautiously pushed her pretty face into view. 'All clear?' She eased her way in. 'Just wanted to ask if Geoff got away to London all right.'

With some effort, Kathryn dragged her thoughts to the present, and smiled at her brother's girl-friend. 'Come in. Yes, he was late as usual, but I got him out of the front door just in time to catch the London train.'

Helen looked at Jon's door. 'What's he like, your new boss? I hear he's a dish. Is he married, engaged or otherwise involved? There's not one unattached female member of the staff who isn't agog to know.'

Kathryn stared at her typewriter keys. 'I couldn't tell you. I haven't taken an interest in his private life.'

Helen looked at her watch. 'Must fly. Tell me all the gossip when you hear it, won't you? 'Bye.'

So he was the subject of girlish speculation. That, Kathryn supposed, was only to be expected. But had he a wife somewhere? She corrected herself—a second wife somewhere? She buried her thoughts beneath the pile of correspondence which she pulled towards her. The internal telephone rang. She grabbed the receiver to silence the noise which tore her nerves to shreds.

'Dr. Wright's secretary here. Can I help you?'

'This is Miss Smith, principal's secretary.' Kathryn visualised the forbidding bespectacled lady at the other end of the line and made a wry face. 'The principal wishes to know if you are busy or whether you could spare him a few minutes.'

'Yes, of course. Shall I go to him or——'

'No, Miss Swale. He will call on you in about five minutes.'

As she stared into space wondering what Francis wanted to see her about, the inner door opened.

'Sorry to interrupt you when you're working so hard——' Kathryn winced at yet another pinprick. '—but I have unaccountably lost my pen. Have you seen it?'

She frowned uncertainly. 'I don't think I have.' She searched frantically in the drawers of her desk, in her letters tray, even in her handbag, knowing that all the time Jon was standing there watching her with sardonic amusement. As a last resort she delved into the pile of papers which she had removed from his desk the day before to sort them for filing. She found it there, and held it out to him, smiling guiltily. 'Sorry.'

He examined it closely as though he had never seen it before. 'This surely is an ominous sign that my secretary's super-efficiency is not always so super.' He turned at the door and taunted her yet again, 'Or did you perhaps have some deep-seated Freudian motive for depriving me of my pen?'

Her face flamed at the question and she banged shut the drawers she had opened in her search.

'Kathryn?' The principal appeared at the door. 'Busy, my dear?' He saw Jon and extended his hand. 'Ah, Dr. Wright. How are you getting on? Coping, no doubt, with the help of my charming fiancée?' He looked at her fondly.

Jon's face was wooden. 'I've heard she's the essence of efficiency.'

'Well, I know I shouldn't speak too highly of her, as I could be accused of prejudice in her favour, but I've heard so much about her capabilities, it's difficult to remember them all.' He smiled smugly. 'I would venture to say that I believe efficiency to be one of the prime attributes not only of a good secretary, but of a good wife.'

Jon's face registered polite amazement. 'Would you indeed? I should have thought that there were other—assets which were more important.'

Kathryn stole a look at them both, and her brain started in a frightening way to grope for a half-hidden truth which tortured her by its elusiveness and worried her by its sudden importance.

19

Watching Francis, his short rotundity contrasting like a carica-
ture with the tall, lean strength of her former husband, she
knew that the explosive feelings which she had buried deep in
the vaults of her mind would before long clamour to be released
from bondage, and if she ever allowed them to see the light of
day, they would blow sky-high the rock-like foundation upon
which her future with Francis was based.

CHAPTER II

'OH no, my dear fellow,' Francis was saying, pouting with his
ample stomach, 'that is where your inexperience lets you down.
You have never been married, so you have a lot to learn, Dr.
Wright.' He patted Kathryn affectionately on the head as
though she were a child. 'This will be my second venture into
wedded bliss, and I can only hope it will be as pleasing and
gratifying as my first turned out to be.'

Kathryn saw Jon's half-concealed gesture of disgust. She
took a deep breath and quickly interrupted her fiancé's musings.

'What did you want to see me about, Francis?'

Jon turned on his heel and left them.

'Ah yes, my dear. About that house we are interested in.
George Creswell tells me that the couple concerned are making
one more attempt to secure a mortgage, but he thinks they
haven't got a chance. As soon as he hears from them, he will let
me know, and we can view it.'

'I see. It's—it's quite exciting to think in terms of a new
house, I must admit.' Anything, she thought, to re-establish that
sense of security which felt so threatened a few moments ago.

The principal pushed open the head of department's door.
'We must have a chat soon, Dr. Wright, about your duties as
vice-principal. I'll give you a ring when I'm free.'

When the principal had gone, Jon reappeared. 'Now that
you have finished granting an audience to your friends and
future next-of-kin, perhaps you will condescend to grant me
one in my room. With the morning's post.'

Forcing herself to ignore the sarcasm, she arranged the letters
in a neat pile, tapped on his door and entered. He was stand-

ing at the window, staring out, apparently lost to the world, and started slightly when he saw her. He sat at his desk and as she leaned across to place the letters in front of him, he stiffened and drew away from her. Her heart did a swallow dive. How long is he going to treat me as though I had an infectious disease? she wondered miserably, and began to walk away.

'Where do you think you're going, Miss Swale?'

'Back to my office.'

'Oh no, you're not. Remain here, please, to explain the contents of these letters. That is part of your job, is it not?'

'Well, I assumed after your instructions about the post yesterday that you wouldn't be needing any help from me in that respect.'

'Oh, did you? If you honestly misinterpreted my instructions, then I'm sorry, but if you do in fact possess the intelligence which others, who seem to know you better, insist that you have, then I can only assume that it was wilful misinterpretation on your part. Come back here, and wait, in case I need your assistance.'

Kathryn stood at his desk, fuming and restless, determined not to sit until invited to do so, but he seemed equally determined to keep her standing.

He read the first letter. 'Are you able to explain this to me?'

She leaned across the desk, endeavouring to read the words upside down, and as she did so her hair fell forward and downwards and brushed his face. He recoiled again and irritably told her, 'Don't do that. Come round here.'

She did as she was told and stood obediently by his side. He handed her the letter. As she read it, he tapped his pencil impatiently on the desk top. 'Well?'

'Yes, I know what this is about. Would you like me to get the appropriate file? The matter should then be self-explanatory.'

He inclined his head. She searched in his filing cabinet and within seconds extracted the file she was looking for. He seemed surprised at her speed, but no word of praise passed his lips.

She stood beside him again, but even that displeased him. 'Bring a chair next to me. And for heaven's sake stop hovering!'

She did as she was told, a lump rising to her throat at his intractable attitude.

With her quick and able assistance, and the files she produced

21

so speedily, he soon dealt with the remaining letters. He thanked her grudgingly for her help.

She smiled at him sweetly. 'As you said yourself, Dr. Wright, that's my job and what I'm paid for. In any case, I was especially detailed by my fiancé to give you all possible assistance, as he considered it very likely that you would need extra help at first, because you are so new to the administrative side of technical education. So you see, I did it to please him.'

She walked back to her office, being rewarded before she went by the sight of his hands being clenched into tight, white-knuckled fists.

'One up to you, *Miss* Swale,' he flung at her just before the door clicked shut behind her.

She was half-way through the letters Jon had dictated when she realised it was time for coffee. She wondered if she should tell him. As his secretary, she decided she must. She tapped on his door and went in.

'Yes?'

'I don't know whether you're interested, but coffee is served every morning at this time in the staff dining-room. Would you like me to show you the way?'

He hesitated, looked at her uncertainly, and ran his tongue over dry lips. 'Well, I could do with a cup.' He eased himself out of his chair. 'All right, show me the way.'

Need he be so ungracious about it? she thought, as she walked beside him along the corridor and up the stairs. It was break-time for the students, too, and one of them called to her, 'We're after contributions for the rag magazine, Miss Swale. Any offers?'

But she waved him away. 'Sorry, Bob, ask my brother, Mr. Swale, engineering department. He might give you a few jokes —all printable, of course.'

The student laughed and went on his way. Another pushed his way across the crowded corridor and asked her, 'Miss Swale, you in this play the drama group's putting on?'

She did not want to delay Jon by stopping to chat, so she answered over her shoulder, 'Might be, Don, if I can find the time.'

Jon looked bewildered at her popularity, but made no comment.

She opened the swing door of the dining-room and let him pass in front of her. 'Coffee is served by a waitress,' she told him. 'It's lunches that are self-service.'

He looked round dubiously at the sea of faces which turned to inspect him. 'Where do I sit?'

'Anywhere you like.' She waited for him to move from her side, but he seemed rooted to the spot. She felt an irresistible urge to say something which she knew she should not, but the temptation was too great. Realising that the circumstances would protect her, she whispered, 'Or would you like me to hold your hand?'

He turned astonished eyes towards her, then she walked away and left him. 'One up to me, Miss Swale,' she told herself, and sat next to her friend from the general office.

'Hallo, Jill. How's life? Had a good Christmas?'

'Fine, thanks. You look very pleased with yourself, Kath,' Jill commented. 'Was that your new boss you came in with? Looks super. What's he like?'

Kathryn looked round and saw that Jon had chosen an empty table by the window, and was looking out of it in a lonely, friendless sort of way. She had to force herself not to feel sorry for him.

'He's all right. And I'll tell you straight away, I don't know if he's married or not.'

The younger girl groaned. 'And here we all are, with our matrimonial tongues hanging out, waiting for the answer to that oh-so-vital question!'

Kathryn stole another look at him, and saw that he was gulping his coffee as if he could not get back to his room fast enough. His gaze roamed across the heads of the other members of staff and as he spotted her, their eyes clashed and locked. Her heart did a somersault. She turned her head quickly and covered up her confusion by talking to her companions. They laughed, although she was not aware that what she had said was funny, and she heard him scrape back his chair and leave. She bit her lip. She knew he would assume that she had been making fun of him.

As she drank her coffee, she wondered why no one had approached him. Members of staff usually made a point of being friendly to newcomers. She pushed away her cup and left her friends. As she walked past some of the teachers, one of

23

them stopped her.

'What's he like, this new boss of yours?'

'He's—he's fine,' she managed to say. 'Why didn't you speak to him and find out for yourselves?'

'We didn't like to. He is the vice-principal, as well as a department head, and anyway, he's not really one of us, is he? He's come out of industry and stepped right into a top job.'

Kathryn raised her eyebrows. 'I don't see what difference that makes.'

When she returned to her room, Jon was standing at the door. 'You're late back, Miss Swale.'

'I'm sorry to disagree, Dr. Wright, but I'm one minute early. Your watch must be fast.'

He took two or three paces towards her. 'And any more cheeky remarks like the one you shot at me in the dining-room, and you'll get exactly what you deserve.'

'I'm sorry if I was cheeky.' She began to type, making further conversation impossible. He seemed mollified by her apology, and left her.

The afternoon passed tranquilly. Jon returned from his teaching session at four-thirty and called Kathryn into his office.

'There are one or two questions I should like to ask you. Please sit down.'

She watched him while he sorted his papers into different piles and put his pencils and ruler into a drawer. Kathryn found the prolonged silence unnerving, and wondered what was coming this time.

At last he spoke. 'Tell me, is it correct that your brother is a lecturer in the engineering department? If so, why have I not seen him?'

'Yes, he works here, but he's away today and tomorrow attending a course in London.'

'I see.' He swivelled slowly from side to side. 'Let me see, how old is he now?'

'Twenty-five. He was fifteen when——' She stopped, not knowing whether he would like her to refer to the past.

'When——?'

'When you left to go to America.'

'Precisely. I too can do arithmetic.'

She coloured at his sarcasm, to which she still could not

24

accustom herself.

'And you are now——?'

'You don't remember?' She could hardly believe he had really forgotten.

'No.' His voice rose a fraction, asking the question, 'Should I remember?'

'Well, I was seventeen and a half when we—when you left. Now I'm nearly twenty-seven.'

'So you are.' His dark eyes appraised her. 'It's all a very long time ago. Where are you living?'

'In the same house as you—as we have always lived.'

'Alone?'

'No, with Geoff. My grandmother died eighteen months ago.'

'I'm sorry to hear that. She was a good woman.'

'She was wonderful.' Kathryn paused for a moment, then continued, 'The house and its contents were left to my brother and myself. That's all there was. No money.'

'Is the house divided into two?'

'Well, Geoff has a couple of rooms upstairs. I have the down-stairs rooms. And the kitchen, of course.'

She was becoming impatient with his cross-examination, and the tone of her voice showed it. However, he chose to ignore her irritation.

'You have a car?'

'No.'

'Geoff?'

'No. He can drive, but we couldn't—really—afford one. The house is rather expensive to run. It's so large.'

'What will happen when you marry?'

She stared at him. 'How can he sit there,' she thought, 'for-getting all the love and passion we once shared, and calmly talk of my coming marriage to another man?'

She stood up. 'He's unofficially engaged, and will no doubt be getting married himself some time. We haven't discussed the problem yet. We shall meet it when the time comes.'

He rose, and indicated with a nod of the head that she could go.

'Goodnight, Dr. Wright.'

'Goodnight, Miss Swale.'

During the short journey home on the bus, she attempted to bring some order to her chaotic thoughts. What had that catechism been about? Why the sudden interest in her affairs?

She spent an unhappy evening brooding about the past, trying almost in vain to recall what it had been like to be married to Jon so many years ago.

Next morning, she helped him with the post again. He was distant and formal and she found his coldness almost harder to bear than his outright hatred of her.

Without warning, he produced a piece of college notepaper and pointed to the printed heading. ' "All replies to be addressed to the principal," ' he read out. 'What in heaven's name does that mean?'

'It means what it says, that all letters, no matter who signs them, which are sent out from the college, receive replies addressed to the principal, and not to the writer of the letter.'

'But what a shocking waste of time. Do you mean to tell me that there are some girls solemnly sitting in the college office opening every single envelope addressed to one man, simply trying to discover from the letter inside who should actually receive it?'

'That's right.'

'Well, I'm sorry. If that is the case, I refuse to conform. In future you will cross out that particular instruction on each piece of notepaper and type in "please reply to the undersigned".'

Kathryn was horrified at his anarchy. 'Surely you should ask the principal's permission first?'

She was quite unprepared for the fury with which he turned upon her. 'Consult the principal? Why the devil should I? No, you'll do as I say, please, without argument, without question.' Contempt entered his eyes. 'And no running to the principal with tales.'

Frightened by his anger, she tried to placate him. 'I suppose—they didn't have that sort of thing in industry?'

'No, Miss Swale, they do not have that damn-fool arrangement in industry. If they did, this country would have failed economically years ago. Imagine all the replies being addressed to the managing director of a firm the size of the one I was working for!'

She was so upset by the ferocity of his temper she found she was still shaking when she returned to her office. It saddened

26

her that ten years had brought about such a disastrous change in his character.

At coffee-time, she found enough courage to tap on his door. 'Are you going to coffee, Dr. Wright?'

He looked a little uncomfortable. 'Not this morning.'

'I'll—I'll introduce you to the others, if you wish.'

'No, thank you. I'd rather drink water here than go up there again. Tell me, are members of staff usually so unfriendly to newcomers? Or is it just me they object to?'

She flushed slightly, and was annoyed with herself for doing so, because she knew it would make him think she was at the bottom of it. 'I think it's because you've come straight from industry into a top teaching job. So I heard, anyway.'

'You heard? It wouldn't, of course, be poison injected into their minds by you, would it?'

She paled at this, but assumed nonchalance. 'If it pleases you to think that, go ahead.'

She turned and left him, but as she drank her coffee with her friends, her mind wandered away from their gossip to the man sitting alone in his room. He was like a small boy, she mused, afraid to venture out to get what he plainly longed for, in case his colleagues rejected him again. A sweet kind of pity flooded through her, and she finished her coffee quickly, excused herself from her friends and went into the kitchen.

'Could you give me a cup of coffee to take to my new boss?' she whispered to Mary, the waitress. 'He's too shy to come up here himself.'

This touched Mary's soft heart. 'Of course, dearie. Here, take him a large cup.'

'You're a dear, Mary. How much?'

Mary told her. She took the money from her purse, and gave it to her, then walked back to her office, carrying the steaming liquid with great care.

She tapped on his door and went in. 'Coffee?' She walked across the room, trying not to spill any into the saucer, and lowered it on to his desk. She was rewarded with the warmest smile he had yet given her.

'Angel!' It was a spontaneous exclamation which came straight from the heart, uncensored by his conscious mind. He raised grateful eyes and saw the answering pleasure in hers. He

27

realised then what he had said. The light in his own suffered an immediate power cut and cynicism elbowed its way back.

'The act of an—almost—perfect secretary. You're not, by any chance, trying to ingratiate yourself into my good books?' he said nastily.

Tears welled up in her eyes and she did not try to hide them. 'Just how unpleasant can you get?' Her voice was thick with emotion.

'Unpleasant?' he drawled. 'But this is nothing. I can be a great deal nastier than this—especially to someone who, like you, has in the past inflicted on me such an incalculable amount of misery and pain. I have a very unforgiving nature.' He leaned back and mercilessly watched her tears. 'And every time I see you cry, I know that I've had just a little bit more of my own back.'

She stared at him through blurred eyes. She whispered, 'You can't, you surely can't be as warped as that!'

'Can't I?' His voice was dead. 'I think you'd better go.' He pushed aside the untouched coffee.

By the time the evening came, Kathryn was longing for her brother's return. He was her ally, the friend to whom she could turn in moments of stress.

He was late and he was tired. He was also hungry and made short work of the meal Kathryn had prepared for him. He asked how things had gone for her at work.

She mumbled, 'Could have been worse.'

He looked at her pale face. 'Now come on, out with it. What went wrong today? Did Jon put you through a mincer?'

She gave him a stricken look. 'Oh, Geoff, you don't know what it's like. He treats me as if I were a bit of rubbish to be walked on. He's carrying on a personal vendetta against me. You could almost call it persecution.'

'Oh, come on now, Kath, don't get melodramatic. Your imagination's working overtime.'

'Imagination? I certainly don't imagine the insults he throws my way every time we meet, which is pretty often.'

'But why, Kath? What's his motive? If he really disliked you, he simply wouldn't bother with you, wouldn't even bother to be nasty to you, would he? But if he still——' He stopped and eyed her speculatively.

'Still what?' She hardly seemed to hear what he was saying, she was so immersed in her unhappy thoughts.

'Oh, nothing. Nothing.' He moved to an armchair. 'Don't mind if I relax down here a bit, before I go up to my room?'

She shook her head. 'It's nice to have you back.'

'You're a nice sister to say that. Look, I'll come and see him in the morning. Has he asked about me, by the way?'

'Yes. Listen, Geoff, he doesn't want anyone at all, and that includes Helen, to know of my past relationship with him. He was quite nasty about it. So I promised on your behalf that neither you nor I would tell a single person. Geoff, you must keep that promise, for my sake.'

'If you both feel so strongly about it, I suppose I'll have to keep mum, but I'd rather not. I tell Helen most things.'

'But not this, Geoff, please.'

'Oh, all right. But we'll have to try to sort out your troubles. Can't have you miserable like this.' He got up. 'Thanks for the meal, Kath. Just what I needed.'

Next morning, Jon was standing at her side as she typed an envelope for him, when her door opened. Jon turned his head impatiently, resenting the interruption. Then he tensed and pure delight seemed to take possession of him. 'Geoff!' He moved towards the newcomer, hands outstretched.

'Jon!' Geoff's face was alight as his hands came out to meet the other man's. 'Boy, is it good to see you again! You know, Jon, you haven't changed a bit.'

'You don't think so? Well, my outer casing may be the same, but, brother, have I grown older and wiser inside! You, Geoff, I must say it, although you'll probably slay me, but my, how you've grown!'

The laughed, they shook hands, and the pleasure they both felt in their reunion was beginning to communicate itself to Kathryn, who sat and watched them with astonished eyes. She could not get over the change in Jon. He seemed years younger, he looked a different man. He even talked differently—to her brother. His behaviour towards Geoff brought into even sharper focus his unpleasant attitude towards her.

'Come into my office, Geoff. We'll have a natter. How long have you got?'

'I've got a free period.'

Jon turned to Kathryn, and his expression and the tone of his voice underwent a metamorphosis. 'I don't want to be disturbed for the next half-hour,' he snapped. 'Is that clear?'

She nodded. Now perhaps Geoff would understand what she was talking about. But he had already gone into Jon's room and had heard nothing. She worked sporadically, typing and listening, typing a little more and listening again. She could not hear what they were saying, but their loud laughter, alternating with quiet discussion, only increased her sadness, and intensified the feeling that she was shut out, on the other side, not even looking in.

The telephone rang and it was a call requiring Jon's attention. She was uncertain whether to interrupt him or tell the caller he was out. Finally, she decided to brave his anger—after all, her brother was there to shield her—and tapped gently on his door and opened it.

Jon was on to her like a guard-dog after an intruder. 'I thought I told you I didn't want to be disturbed?'

'I'm- I'm sorry, Dr. Wright, but this phone call must receive attention. The Youth Employment Office wishes to have a verbal reference on a student.'

'Oh, blast them. Look, can you deal with it yourself?'

Her smile was saccharin-sweet, her expression innocent, as she asked, 'Using my own initiative, Dr. Wright?'

The flash of anger which flared in his eyes was unseen by Geoff, who was staring at his hands.

'*Touché*, Miss Swale. Using your own initiative, please. If it's no trouble, of course.'

'Will you excuse me, then, while I get the student's file?'

She crossed the room to the filing cabinet near Jon's desk. Geoff stood up and stared out of the window, while Jon swayed gently from side to side in his chair and watched her with lazy eyes. She jerked open the drawer of the cabinet, selected the correct folder with lightning fingers and returned swiftly to her room. She picked up the receiver and closed her ears to the noise which had started again as soon as she left the two men alone. With speed and efficiency, she read out to the caller the relevant details from the student's file.

She was so busy with her work that she was late for morning coffee. She resolutely turned away from Jon's door and hurried out, determined this morning to do no good deed as far as he was concerned. But as she went into the dining-room, she was so surprised to see him sitting among a group of his colleagues —Geoff was one of them—that she let the door swing back on to her shoulder. Rubbing it ruefully, she went across to her friends' table, noticing with dismay that Jon was sitting across the gangway from where Jill Summers had kept a seat for her.

They were already half-way through their coffee, and Kathryn looked around anxiously for the waitress. She dreaded being left alone at the table.

'Hallo, Kath,' Jill greeted her. 'You look like a thunderstorm that's lost its way. Cheer up.'

'Do I? I'm not surprised. If I were a weather map, I'd be full of depressions.' The girls laughed loudly and one or two others, including Jon, looked their way.

Jill whispered to Kathryn, 'I see our Annette has her claws into the new head of department. And it doesn't look as if he's fighting very hard for his freedom, either.'

Liz Williams, another typist from the general office, shielded her face with her hand and said, 'She's giving him the great big green light. Someone ought to warn the poor chap that where our Annette's concerned, it's green, not red, for danger. I wouldn't like to trust that female with a man of mine. Can't you warn him, Kath? He's your boss, and he looks too nice to be left to her tender mercies.'

Kathryn shrugged and fiddled with the sugar bowl. 'He's my boss, yes, but not my responsibility. Let him find out for himself.'

But her casual words belied her true feelings, which were tied up in knots. Her heart cried out, 'She's like a great and dangerous whirlpool. She's drawing him in. He'll soon be lost to me.'

Mary arrived at last with the coffee. She waved her hand at the money Kathryn offered her. 'Pay me later, dearie. I'm all behind today.'

By the time the liquid was cool enough to drink, Kathryn's friends had gone. Having no one to talk to, she was forced to listen to the discussion which was proceeding at the next table.

She glanced at Jon and saw that his attention was completely absorbed by the beautiful young woman at his side. He was openly admiring her jet-black hair, drawn back loosely and tied

31

with a bright red chiffon scarf. He certainly liked her large brown eyes which shone into his, and her well-shaped lips, which now and then daintily puffed out clouds of cigarette smoke. When they were not puffing, they were pouting, and her speaking voice had a husky, intimate quality which charmed the listener. There was no doubt at all that her present listener was charmed beyond words.

'Did your wife mind moving to the Midlands from Lancashire, Dr. Wright?'

Annette Linton's subtle way of discovering Jon's status in life was answered bluntly and to Annette's complete satisfaction.

'I have no wife.'

Kathryn heard the reply, spoken distinctly and in a voice he knew would carry. He made the word 'wife' sound almost distasteful.

'I'm what is usually described as an eligible "bachelor".

'A bachelor?' Fred Welford was astonished. 'Now, how did a nice-looking fellow like you manage to escape the clutches of a female for so long?' He leaned back and patted his stomach. 'I was caught when I was twenty. Never ceased regretting it.'

Annette tapped the ash from her cigarette, and frowned disbelievingly. 'Now, Mr. Welford, you know that's not true. Not only do you look well fed . . .'

'Call me Fred Wellfed and be done with it,' he interrupted, laughing with the others at his own joke.

'—but you look well cared for and, may one say, well loved?' Annette looked again at Jon and gave him a wink full of meaning.

'He's lapping it up,' thought Kathryn moodily. 'How can he fall for that sort of talk? She's a line-shooter, surely he can see that.' She caught her brother's eye and he frowned and turned down his mouth. Kathryn knew he could not stand Annette Linton and was obviously hating to see Jon, whom he once hero-worshipped and for whom he still had a high regard, falling for her hook, line and sinker.

Mr. Welford was saying, 'But personal experience apart, I don't hold with young marriages. My son wants to marry a girl this coming summer. He's twenty—still at university, and I told him, "Wait, son, a couple of years at least. If you do what I did, you'll live to regret it!"'

32

'Now, Mr. Welford, if I had been your wife, I should at that point have thrown something at you good and hard. Fight back, that's my motto.' Annette's eyes delved into Jon's. 'Especially men.'

They smiled at each other.

'It's said that young marriages don't last.' Jon threw his controversial statement into the argument with a secret smile. 'Statistics prove it.'

Jim Mexby, head of commerce, eased his long frame into the chair opposite Annette's and signalled to the waitress for his coffee. 'They do say that more youthful marriages than mature ones end up in divorce.' He smiled knowingly at Annette. 'Since you're definitely not in the teenage category, Annette, by the time you've finished sowing your wild oats and finally pick out Mr. Right er- apologies to Dr. Wright here—you'll be all set for a marriage which lasts, won't you?'

Annette's eyes fluttered coyly at the speaker. 'Wild oats, Mr. Mexby? Oh, but women don't sow wild oats.'

Kathryn saw Jon flick a glance at the girl's beautiful face with more than a spark of interest. 'Oh? What would you call it, then?'

Annette turned her large eyes and looked into Jon's with subtle intimacy. 'I, Dr. Wright, would prefer to call them, say, a series of romantic interludes—more feminine, don't you think? More intriguing, perhaps?'

'Intrigue is right, where you're concerned,' muttered Geoff, who obviously felt he had been silent too long.

'Now, Geoff, you're giving our new head of department the impression that I have something of a reputation where men are concerned.' She smiled at Jon again. 'That's hardly fair, is it, Dr. Wright?'

'I don't know.' He looked at her reflectively, assessing her in detail and clearly finding the summing-up worth while. 'It may act as an incentive to me to find out for myself.'

A chortle of triumph escaped from Annette's throat, and Geoff snorted in disgust. He rose. 'I'm off. I have work to do. Coming?' he asked Jon.

'You carry on, Geoff.' Jon waved him away. 'I'll follow later. My interest has been aroused.' Again he contemplated Annette.

Kathryn had heard enough. She scraped back her chair so loudly that Jon turned to look. He saw her flushed and angry face and narrowed his eyes as he watched her looking for Mary to pay for her coffee. Then Kathryn heard Annette say, 'By the way, Dr. Wright, my name's Annette—to you.'

'Mine is Jon,' was the immediate reply. 'Call me that.'

'Watch it, Dr. Wright.' Mr. Mexby rose and pushed in his chair. 'She's got you sighted in her radar screen. Before you know where you are, you'll be brought down in flames by those laser beams in her big eyes.'

'You think so? I'm not thirty-two and unattached for nothing, you know. I can take evasive action with the best of them at the moment of kill. Years of bachelorhood teach a man how to be elusive.' He shot a challenging glance at Annette who, surprisingly, coloured under his keen gaze.

Jim Mexby shrugged and walked away. He called over his shoulder, 'You have been warned.'

CHAPTER III

As Kathryn made her way back to her office, she struggled with her temper and put it on a leash. She was sidetracked from her unhappy thoughts by a group of noisy students, who surrounded her as if they had kidnap intentions and demanded an interview with her on the spot. There was still no sign of Jon, so she darted into a classroom to look at the wall-clock.

'According to that, there's seven minutes of your break-time left. Come to my office and I'll see you there, my boss permitting.'

They sped along the corridor and down the stairs, Kathryn racing with them, and she preceded them into her room. Gasping for breath, she asked them what they wanted.

Maureen, a pretty young art student, spoke first. 'To put it briefly, Miss Swale, we would like you to be the leading lady in our play. It's an old Russian comedy, translated into English. You've been in our plays before, so please, Miss Swale, would you do the part for us?'

David Hickley, students' union secretary, backed her up. 'If you'll do it, Miss Swale, you'll be the main draw. You're just right in colouring, build, looks, the lot. We name it, you've got it.'

Kathryn laughed at his flattery. 'It all depends—is it a big part, and would I be able to learn the words in time?'

They reassured her that it was easily within her capabilities, and used pressure and persuasion in increasing doses until eventually she agreed to their request.

'Having got that settled,' Maureen said, 'could you find us a hero? What about your fiancé—is he someone on the staff? Would he do it?'

Kathryn thought this so amusing she began to laugh, and as the irony struck her—that her fiancé was so far removed from the hero-figure they had obviously concocted for her, they would have been horrified if they had known the truth—her laughter became almost hysterical. There was an impatient sound from the other office, and the students looked round.

'Who's that?' Maureen whispered. 'Your boss? Would he do the part? Can't you ask him?'

Again Kathryn thought this was an ironic joke, but this time she did not laugh. 'Absolutely no. Look, it's time I started work. You too. I've agreed to be the heroine, but you must produce your own hero.'

'But if we choose one, Miss Swale, you'll have to vet him. After all, you'll be the one who has to kiss him.'

'*Kiss* him? I never bargained for that.'

'But all heroines kiss the heroes, don't they?'

Laughing again, Kathryn shooed them from her room, just as Jon's door opened. He looked irritated.

'What was that all about? You seemed to find it excruciatingly funny.'

Kathryn explained. He looked comically indignant.

'Me act the part of the hero? No thanks. I would agree to do that only on condition that I'd be allowed to choose my own heroine. Unfortunately, it seems as though the heroine has already been chosen, and their choice most decidedly would not be mine.'

Kathryn bit her lip.

The telephone rang. A husky female voice grated against Kathryn's ear. 'Is Dr. Wright available, please?'

'Who's speaking?' As if I didn't know, Kathryn thought.

'Just put me through to him.'

She handed Jon the receiver. 'A woman wants you. Won't give her name.'

'That sounds distinctly promising. Hallo, Jon Wright here. Oh, Annette. Yes? Tonight?' He sounded pleased. 'Yes, I'm free. At your place? Fine. Yes, I'd appreciate some home cooking.' He lowered his eyes pointedly to Kathryn. 'Haven't had that luxury for years. You know, living in hotels and all that. Time? Address?' He scribbled on a piece of paper. 'Right, I'll be there.'

He dropped the receiver on to its cradle. 'My word, that woman is a fast worker! What's her surname? I didn't catch it when we were introduced. What's her job?'

'She's Annette Linton. She's head of the domestic science department. And,' she tossed at him before she could stop herself, 'she's a man-eater.'

Jon's broad smile irritated his secretary intensely. 'Now that makes me even more eager to go. Man-eater?' His eyes took on a faraway look. 'I can imagine no greater ecstasy than to be consumed by those beautiful and very feminine jaws.' He looked askance at her. 'And speaking from a purely personal angle, the hungrier and greedier she is, the better I shall like it.'

Kathryn began to type. She held in her irritation, her exasperation and her misery and wished he would go away. He did.

'What did Jon tell you this morning, Geoff?' Kathryn asked later. 'You were in there long enough to have exchanged personal histories from the year dot.'

'Oh, he told me quite a lot.' Geoff was evasive as he sat by the roaring fire in Kathryn's living-room. 'Can't remember it all. It appears that after you—broke with him, he went a bit haywire, had one girl-friend after another. Then he came back to England, worked for his Ph. D. and got it. He found a job in industry and stayed with the same firm all the time, being promoted eventually to quite a high position for his age. Then he took the job here at the technical college. That's about it.' He paused, looked sideways at his sister.

'He—he asked me about the "other man", Kath.' he said, hesitantly.

She turned anxious eyes to him. 'What did you tell him?'

'Said I was too young at the time to know what was going on.

And anyway, it wasn't my business. I told him to ask you, if he really wanted to know.'

'What did he say to that?'

'Mumbled something like "not on your life" and changed the subject.'

'You mustn't ever tell him, Geoff. Promise me you never will.'

Geoff shrugged. 'I still think you're being a complete idiot. But it's your business.' He hesitated, then said, 'He's invited me to dinner on Sunday evening at his hotel.'

'On my birthday? Did you accept?'

He nodded. 'Didn't think you'd mind. You're going to the Old Boy's place, aren't you?'

'I'm going to Francis' house, yes, so I don't mind if you go. Where's he staying?'

'Don't you know? At the Continental.'

'What? The largest hotel in the town? How can he afford that?'

'Seems he can. He said he's had no one to spend his money on all these years, so he's just left it in the bank to accumulate. Have you seen his car? It's a white Jag. One of the new ones. New, mark you. Mint condition.'

'By the way, did you know he's been invited to Annette's this evening?'

'What?' Geoff was aghast. 'Already? He only met her this morning.'

She smiled, remembering Jon's comment. 'As he said himself, when he received the invitation, she works fast.'

Geoff shook his head. 'I'll have to warn him.'

'It's no good. I've tried. Made him more eager, he said.' She sighed. 'Well, go on. What else did he say?'

'Only that he's looking for a furnished flat. Can't remember any more.' He rose and stretched. 'Got some homework to mark before Helen comes. Thanks for the tea, Kath.'

So, Kathryn thought, as she washed the dishes, he has invited my brother to dinner, but not my brother's sister. The wound that was somewhere in the region of her heart became just a little deeper, and just a little less easy to bear.

Kathryn made a determined effort to be early next morning. She was hanging up her coat when she heard raised voices in the head of department's room. One of them was Jon's; the other, she realised with surprise, was her brother's. No wonder he had rushed out immediately after breakfast. He had wanted to arrive before she did.

She sat at her desk and did her best to shut out their words, but they spoke so loudly she could not help overhearing.

'Who put you on to this?' Jon was saying, 'your precious sister? I thought so. Well, if I didn't know she hated the very ground I walked on, I'd say she was jealous. You can tell her from me to keep out of my private affairs.'

'She only had your interests at heart, Jon.'

'After what she did to me nearly ten years ago? You have to be joking.' He stopped, but, receiving no response, continued, 'Look, old chap, you're a man. When a woman like Annette positively throws herself at you, what normal unattached male, which I am, would run the other way? I'm only human, Geoff.'

'Well, I'm just warning you. That woman's poison.'

'Yes, but what poison, and what a wonderful way to die!'

'Be cynical if you like, but I don't know how you, a man of high principles, can overlook the doubtful morals of a woman like her, when, on the other hand, you can't seem to forgive...'

Jon cut him off. 'Geoff, I wouldn't even begin to put a wife of mine, from whom I would expect the highest standards of moral behaviour, into the same category as a woman of Annette's calibre.' There appeared to be a short silence. Then, 'Don't worry about me, Geoff. I can, if necessary, play the lady at her own game. I've become adept at it over the years. I'm a hard nut to crack these days, boy, and she knows it. That's why she's so interested.'

Geoff seemed to capitulate. 'Well, I suppose you know what you're doing, but——'

'I'm sorry, Geoff, but where women are concerned, I'm a complete cynic now. I'm immune. I take them as they come— and go. Thanks, though, for your concern. I appreciate it, but it's misplaced. I can look after myself. But, after your sister, I'll never trust another woman again.'

Kathryn heard Jon's other door close and supposed it was her brother leaving. The inner door opened. Jon stood there. 'How long have you been in here?'

She did not look at him. 'Long enough.'

'Have you been listening to our conversation?'

38

'Your voices carried, Dr. Wright. I could hardly help it.'

'Then you deserved everything you got. You know what they say about eavesdroppers.'

'But I——'

He slammed the door on her words.

A few minutes later, her internal telephone rang. 'Dr. Wright's secretary here.'

'Is that so?' came the sarcastic reply. 'Then Dr. Wright wants you at once.'

She appeared at his door. 'You—want me, Dr. Wright?'

He heard the sugar in her voice, and gave her a scathing look.

'Don't be pert. It doesn't suit you. Sit down. I want some information from you. Nothing else.'

She dropped her eyes at the expression in his, and sat down.

'Tell me, I'm a new boy at this job. I see there's a member of my staff leaving soon. Is it possible for an existing teacher to be promoted automatically to the vacancy, or does it have to be advertised?'

'In education, every vacancy has to be advertised.'

'Suppose there was someone on the staff whom I considered quite capable of doing the job, what then?'

'It would still have to be advertised. You could, of course, point out to the teacher concerned that the post was vacant, and hope he takes the hint and applies. Even so, the interviewing committee might prefer to appoint someone else.'

'So the poor chap on the staff would be passed over. No doubt he would get a job elsewhere and the college would lose a good teacher. Senseless way of going on. In industry, promotion is usually automatic within the company if the person concerned is good enough.'

'Some people in education, Dr. Wright, consider it better for an educational establishment, especially one concerned with further education, to keep drawing in new blood, in other words, new ideas. If people already on the staff were continually being promoted, the only newcomers would be at the bottom of the scale, and too young to have had any worthwhile experience which would prove valuable to the college or school they join.' She smiled at him disarmingly. 'After all, you were an outsider and came into a top job. Someone on the staff may have been passed over for you. Their ideas were probably nil, compared with yours which are new and challenging, because you've come from the "fresh air" outside.'

'I suppose you're trying to say that doing it my way, that is, promoting internally, would cause a form of educational in-breeding which isn't healthy?'

'Yes, I am.' She looked down at her hands, feeling strangely moved by the atmosphere of equality which had manifested itself as their discussion proceeded. She glanced at him shyly and encountered an odd expression on his face as he regarded her, which turned her heart upside down. She caught her breath and said, rather wildly, 'May I go now?'

He was about to answer when his internal telephone shrilled, shattering utterly the pleasantness between them. He lifted the receiver. 'Yes?' He was abrupt and annoyed. 'Yes, she's here with me.'

'Your fiancé.' He hissed the word, as though hating each syllable.

She leaned across his desk to answer it. 'Hallo, Francis. Yes, Francis, it is. Yes, on Sunday. Yes, I'd love to, thanks.'

Jon apparently could not stand her one-sided conversation any longer. He jerked himself out of his chair and stood at the window.

'Now, Francis?' She stole a look at the head of department's back. 'Well, all right, yes, Francis.' She replaced the receiver.

'Must you keep saying "yes, yes, yes, Francis"?' he enquired of the window pane in front of him. He turned on her. 'Don't you *ever* say "no, Francis"?'

'I'm sorry, Dr. Wright, but he—he wants me in his room. Now.'

'Now? In the middle of my work? What do I do until you get back? Go for a run round the block?'

'I don't think I'll be long. Do you mind?'

'Of course I mind. Oh, go on, go on.' He waved her away impatiently.

Kathryn went along to Miss Smith's room and put her head round the door, but the secretary was missing. Kathryn tapped on the principal's door.

'Come in, my dear,' he called.

His secretary was sitting meekly by his side, taking dictation.

'Sorry to disturb you.' Kathryn thought, with some amusement, 'Quits. Now we've all been disturbed.'

With bad grace, Miss Smith rose and smiled stiffly. Her eyes, behind gold-rimmed spectacles, darted swiftly towards the principal. 'Shall we resume later, sir?'

Kathryn winced. 'Sir,' she called him. How could he encourage her to say that? But he actually seemed to like it.

'Please, Miss Smith. I shall be—oh, about ten minutes at the most.'

Annie Smith skirted round Kathryn as though she was something that had crawled from under the carpet. 'I do believe she's jealous.' The ridiculous, wild thought struck Kathryn so suddenly, she nearly giggled.

'Now, my dear, sit down, do.' Kathryn occupied Miss Smith's chair. "You confirmed on the telephone that your birthday is on Sunday. That bears out what is in my diary. Well, I have here, in my drawer,' he searched at the back of it and withdrew a small, well-wrapped packet, 'my present to you. You may either keep it until Sunday, or open it now, as you wish.'

Kathryn flushed and took the gift with shaking hands. Something deep inside her wanted unaccountably to reject it, to say, 'No, I must not have it. I should be taking it under false pretences.' But she quelled the feeling, resolutely turned her back on her stirring conscience, and removed the layers of tissue paper. She came to a long, narrow box, opened it, and gasped. Inside was an expensive, minute and extremely beautiful gold watch.

Her eyes thanked him before the words came out. 'Oh, Francis, it's wonderful! Thank you, thank you so much. May I—may I put it on?'

'By all means, my dear. Here,' he rose, 'let me fasten it.'

He stood close to her while he slipped the expanding bracelet over her hand and on to her slim wrist. Then he leaned forward and, without warning, kissed her full on the mouth.

Kathryn almost cried out at the unexpected intimate contact. She had to hold herself in with such force that she paled. She wanted to tear the gift off her arm and throw it back at him. He had never done such a thing before. She was aghast at herself, guilt and self-disgust swamping her.

Somehow she remained outwardly calm and smiling, and

even managed to make herself peck him on the face. He was delighted with her action.

'On Sunday evening, my dear, I shall take you out to dinner. Come to my house, please, at seven-thirty, and we shall go on from there. Now, I must continue with my work. Goodbye for now.'

She turned at the door. 'Thank you again, Francis. In fact, I don't know how to thank you.'

'Just by being yourself, my dear, that's all I ask in return.'

She walked slowly up the stairs to her office. She did not feel like facing Jon, and had to steel herself to meet his sardonic gaze. He was standing by her typewriter, fiddling with the keys. He noticed her heightened colour and too-bright eyes, then he saw her watch.

As she stood by him, he took her wrist in cool fingers, and inspected her present. 'That must have cost him a packet.' He looked at her and his expression hardened. 'Now I wonder what Miss Swale had to do to deserve that?'

The pressure of his fingers increased unbearably. She snatched her wrist away and tried to rub out the pain.

'No, don't tell me,' he continued. 'I'd rather not know.'

Wild stallions would not drag the truth from her, just to satisfy his curiosity. She turned away. 'Think what you like.'

She was in no mood for his sarcasm and his barbs. She was still too shattered by the revulsion which had nearly strangled her when Francis had kissed her on the lips for the first time.

It was Sunday afternoon. Kathryn was curled in her armchair in front of the fire, reading. She had made herself a cup of tea, and had nibbled a few biscuits to keep her going until her meal with Francis. She wondered where he would take her; probably to that quiet little restaurant in a side street where they had celebrated their engagement.

She took a quick bath. Then she dressed and applied her make-up with extra care. 'It is my birthday, after all,' she told herself. 'I must try to rise to the occasion however tied up inside I feel.'

She chose from her limited wardrobe a deep pink fine wool dress. The colour emphasised her fair skin and the style flattered her petite figure. As she walked to the bus stop, a gale swirled about her legs. She hugged her fur collar close to her cheeks and hoped the wind would not create too much havoc with her hair-style.

She walked along the path to Francis' front door, rang the bell and waited, almost fearfully, for the door to open.

A tall, fair-haired man stood there and regarded her with surprised interest. 'Yes?'

Taken aback at not being invited in, Kathryn asked, 'Is Francis—is Mr. Rutland available?'

'He is. Who shall I say has called?'

'Kathryn—Kathryn Swale.' She hesitated over her name, feeling puzzled and a little put out at her rather cool reception.

The young man's expression underwent a complete change.

'You're not, you can't be my father's fiancée?'

'I'm sorry,' Kathryn told him in a small voice, 'but I'm afraid I am.'

The door swung open wide. 'Come in, come in. What will you think of me? I'm Max, his son. Surely he's told you about me? Or does he regard me as a skeleton in his cupboard?'

Kathryn laughed as she stepped into the warm lounge.

Max held out his hand. 'First, let's do the thing properly.'

Kathryn put her hand in his. Max gazed at her transfixed.

'It's not every day that one meets one's stepmother-to-be for the first time. What am I saying, you've got me so bemused! My word, my father has better taste than I ever credited him with.'

She gave him a small curtsy. 'Thank you for those few kind words. They were just what my buffeted ego needed.'

'Give me your coat. Make yourself at home. I'll call Dad. He's polishing his shoes.'

His father, it seemed, instructed him to give his future stepmother a drink. As Max handed her a glass of sherry, he stared at her again. 'You know, you can't be a day older than I am. May I enquire your age? Is it done to ask one's stepmother such a thing?'

'It's my twenty-seventh birthday today.'

'Well now, if that isn't a coincidence. My twenty-seventh birthday is on Tuesday.'

'So I'm not a day older than you. I'm two.' Kathryn laughed. She decided she was going to like her stepson very much.

'Are you on holiday?' she asked, smiling up into his face.

He could not keep his eyes off her. 'No. I'm home-based for

the next two or three months. My wanderings around the world have ceased temporarily.'

'Your father tells me you're a chemical engineer.'

'Yes, a roving one. I like it that way. You know. I wish I hadn't got a date this evening. I'd have gate-crashed your tête-à-tête and come with you.'

His father appeared in the doorway.

'Then it's just as well you are otherwise engaged, my son.'

Max turned to him. 'Congratulations, Father, on your choice of fiancée. I couldn't have chosen better myself.'

'Oh dear, your compliments are going to my head faster than this wine.' Kathryn drained her glass and rose. 'Are we going, Francis?'

'Yes, my dear. You look very charming. Worthy of the best hotel in town, I think, especially as we are celebrating your birthday. Max, Kathryn's coat, please?'

Max held it for her as she slipped it on. He released her hand reluctantly as she bade him goodbye.

'We shall beyond doubt meet again soon, Stepmother. That's a promise.'

There was dread in her heart as they left the house—surely they were not going to the Continental? If so, she could hardly persuade her fiancé to change his mind.

Francis' large car nosed its way through the heavy traffic. It was raining heavily, and driving conditions were difficult.

'When we arrive at the Continental, my dear——'

'Is that where we're going, Francis, the Continental?'

'Yes. You haven't been there before, have you? I thought it would be a nice surprise. I've attended dinners there given by local associations and so on. It's an excellent hotel, I can assure you.'

'I don't doubt that, Francis.'

'When we arrive, would you please wait for me in the entrance foyer, while I garage the car?'

'Yes, of course. You won't be long, will you?'

He drew up at the kerb and Kathryn hurried out of the rain through the swing doors, which were held open for her. Francis soon joined her. Their coats were taken to the cloakroom, and they were led to a reserved table near the centre of the dining-room. Their feet sank into soft carpets and Kathryn's eyes were dazzled by brilliant lighting effects and the glamour of the scene

44

in front of her. They settled themselves at the table and studied the menu. She hardly dared to raise her eyes. Somewhere, near or far, sat Jon and Geoff.

After they had made their choice and Francis had given their order, Kathryn found a scrap of courage and looked around her immediate vicinity. Then her eyes became brave and roamed in a wider circle—and stopped short. There they were, at a table across the room, and they had seen her. Geoff raised his hand, Jon turned a scowling face towards them and immediately looked away.

Now Jon knew she was there, and she knew where he was sitting. How could she keep her eyes off him for the rest of the evening? She forced herself to become animated, to appear to enjoy it all, because it was her birthday, and a special occasion.

As the meal progressed, she talked gaily to her fiancé, and he was plainly charmed by her. He smoothed his grey hair and polished his spectacles, and adjusted his tie, and made it plain to anyone who was interested that this happy, beautiful young woman sitting opposite him made him feel many years younger. He was proud of her good looks, proud of her intelligence and proud, above all, that she had consented to become his wife.

'I hope you don't mind, Francis, but I've agreed to act in the students' play. I've been in one of their productions before and I love acting, as you probably know.'

'Of course I have no objection, Kathryn. It will be a pleasure to see you on the stage. Is it a big part?'

'It's the heroine. But the most amusing thing is that they are pressing me to find my own hero. They asked me who my fiancé was, and could I persuade him to act the part?'

Francis threw back his head and laughed. He pointed a finger to his chest. 'Me? Act the part of a hero?' He laughed again. 'What did you tell them?'

'To find their own leading man. I don't know anyone who would do it.'

Francis was still laughing at himself as the male lead in a students' play. He attracted some attention by his prolonged amusement, and Kathryn felt as well as saw Jon's look of anger as he stared at them. Did he think she was doing this for the purpose?

'I've just had a bright thought, my dear,' Francis was saying. 'My son, Max, is an ardent amateur actor. Do you know, he

45

might be persuaded to fill the vacancy, especially when he hears who his leading lady would be.'

Kathryn became excited at the suggestion. He would be all the students could ever want—tall, handsome and debonair.

'Would you ask him, Francis? Perhaps he could give me a ring and tell me his answer.'

'By all means, my dear. Which brings me to another matter. You remember the house our friends the Creswells told us about? Well, it's back on the market. The couple who were interested failed to raise a mortgage. Would you like to view it some time?'

Kathryn thought quickly.

'Well, I know Dr. Wright has to go to the education department on Wednesday morning. While he's out that way, he could probably take me along to have a quick preliminary look at it—if you don't mind, that is.'

'That is an excellent idea. You can tell him he has my permission to take you. He could use my car, in fact, to save on his petrol.'

'I don't know if he would want to do that ... But I'll see what he says.' She glanced with some trepidation across the room at her former husband, who was once again scowling their way.

For some inexplicable reason, she began to relish his annoyance. Why should she not be enjoying herself in this most excellent hotel? He hadn't got a monopoly on it, he didn't own it. With such thoughts she justified her presence there, and shrugged off the anxiety which weighed her down whenever she thought of what he might say to her next morning.

Francis sat back in his chair and eased his rather plump body into a more comfortable position. He seemed to be suffering a little from a surfeit of food. He looked around for the first time and spotted Jon and his guest. He leaned across the table, tapped her hand and said, 'Isn't that Dr. Wright and your brother?'

Kathryn allowed her eyes to wander round the room and settle with simulated surprise on the two men, who were deep in conversation.

'Why, yes, it is. Oh, I remember now—Geoff told me he would be coming here this evening. Dr. Wright is apparently staying here, and invited my brother to dinner.'

46

'I didn't realise they knew each other.'

'They—they played chess together some years ago. They're both chess enthusiasts.'

'Are they? I must challenge them to a game some time. As you know, it's a favourite pastime of mine.' He looked a little puzzled. 'Then if your brother knew him, you too must have made his acquaintance.'

'I was—friendly with his sister.'

'I see.' Then he changed the subject. 'Forgive me for mentioning it now, my dear, but it was pointed out to me by my secretary—and it came as an unpleasant shock—that—er—that you, as Dr. Wright's secretary, were deleting the instruction on the college notepaper that all correspondence should be addressed to me as the principal. Can you explain this?'

Taken completely unawares, Kathryn had to summon her scattered wits, and to give herself time, frowned and pretended innocence. Then she exclaimed, 'Oh, of course, now I know what you're talking about. Dr. Wright told me that the administrative side of industry, which he's just left, was run on very different lines from that of education, and he thought—the instruction only—er—confused matters. He didn't think you'd mind.'

Kathryn knew that she had never wriggled so hard before to get someone off the hook. 'And small thanks I'll get from the head of department in question for my efforts to shield him!'

'I see,' her fiancé said. 'Well, I would appreciate it if you would tell him that I wish this practice to stop, otherwise I should have to let all the others do it, and I could not tolerate that.'

Why don't you tell him yourself? Kathryn wanted to cry out. But she merely answered, 'If you wish me to tell him, I will.'

'One more thing, my dear. I remember Dr. Wright mentioning on the day he was appointed head of department that he was committed to attending a conference in Derbyshire towards the end of this term. Apparently he is one of the organisers and became involved at his last place of work.'

'He hasn't mentioned it to me yet.'

'No doubt he will. As the subject of the conference interests me greatly, could you possibly persuade him to obtain a ticket for me to attend? And if you would like to accompany me, one for you.'

'But—but what interest would I have in a conference like that?'

He patted her hand. 'I should like you to come with me. It would be a break for you and a pleasure for me. You could go either as a visitor or, if that is not possible, as his secretary.'

Kathryn recoiled from asking Jon such a favour. She could imagine his reaction, and she did not care to face it.

Francis smiled into her eyes. 'Would you do that for me, Kathryn? I should be most grateful, my dear.'

'Ask him these favours yourself,' she wanted to beg him. 'Are you so afraid of him that you must use me as a go-between?' But she answered, 'I'll—I'll see what I can do.'

How she would feel when the time came to plead her fiancé's case with the man of whom she too, deep down, was afraid, she could not even begin to imagine.

CHAPTER IV

GEOFF was having his breakfast when Kathryn walked into the kitchen.

'Hallo,' she said. 'Enjoy yourself yesterday?'

'Fine, thanks. You did, too didn't you? Anyone could see—and hear that.'

'What do you mean?'

'You and the Old Boy were making enough noise. I'm warning you, Kath, Jon was livid that you took the Old Boy to the Continental. Why did you, Kath?'

'Why did I? My dear brother, it was the other way round. I had to go there. Francis took me as a pleasant surprise. It was my birthday, remember, or had you forgotten? Anyway, whose side are you on? Has Jon poisoned your mind against me now?'

'Don't be daft, Kath. But you might have chosen somewhere else.'

'If I'd had the choice, I can assure you I wouldn't have gone within a mile of the place knowing that—that man was staying there.'

Geoff merely said 'Don't be daft' again and went on with his breakfast.

Believing that attack was the best form of defence, Kathryn stormed into her office, removed her coat and flicked a comb through her hair. She knocked briefly on the head of department's door and went in. He was plainly taken by surprise. He raised an eyebrow.

'I didn't send for you.'

She fired the first round. 'I understand you were—"livid" was the word my brother used, at my having the audacity to dine last night at *your* hotel.'

'Was I? I was hardly aware of your presence last night.'

Kathryn persisted. 'I expect you thought I did it for the purpose.'

'I have no doubt you did it for the purpose. Having failed to get an invitation out of me, you did the next best thing. You persuaded your fiancé to take you there.' He looked at his watch. 'I'm ready to do some work now.'

She ignored his remark. 'I suppose you think I did it just to annoy you.'

He sighed. 'I'm perfectly sure you did it just to annoy me. Now can we . . .'

'All right, if it gives you any satisfaction to think that, yes, I did do it to annoy you. In fact, I do everything to annoy you. I eat, drink and breathe to annoy you. I live to annoy you, and I would even die to annoy you, just to deprive you of my secretarial services.' Tears welled up and spilled down her cheeks. 'Now does that satisfy you?'

He sighed again and leaned back in his chair. 'Have you quite finished your childish histrionics? You should keep your play-acting for the stage. Look, I'm just a cool, calculating scientist. I try at all times to be rational and detached. To me, emotion is simply an irritating incidental to life, so don't think I'm moved every time you turn on the tears.'

'You- you're not rational. You're prejudiced, overbearing, stupidly blind and as hard as—as reinforced granite!' She was sobbing now and searching madly for a handkerchief.

He produced a clean, folded one from his pocket. 'I think this is the drill, isn't it—you use my handkerchief?'

He waited patiently for her to calm herself and dry her tears.

'I'm—I'm sorry,' she mumbled, after a few minutes, wiping the tears from her eyes.

'Right. Now I know just what you think of me, please can we get on with some work?'

Quite subdued, she stuffed his handkerchief into her pocket. 'I'll wash this and return it.'

'Oh, don't worry about it. I've plenty more.'

She collected her notebook and they began to work.

She was busy typing when the internal telephone disturbed her.

'Kath? Jill here. How went it yesterday? Have a nice birthday?'

'Just a minute, Jill.' Kathryn got up and peeped cautiously into Jon's room. As she thought, he was still away at the head of department's meeting.

'All clear, Jill. Actually, I'm up to my eyes this morning. After these letters, I've got a pile of exam papers to type. What did you want to know?' Jill repeated her question. 'Very nice, thank you. Yes, I had quite a few cards—thanks for yours, by the way—and some lovely flowers from Francis, and his watch, of course. I showed you that, didn't I? Geoff and Helen gave me a heavenly sweater. It was so cold, I wore it all day yesterday. And in the evening, Francis took me to the Continental, no less. It was a complete surprise. I've never been there before. It's marvellous, Jill. You should find an affluent boy-friend to take you there some time.'

They laughed together. 'Incidentally, I met Francis' son. Yes, he has one. My age, exactly. All you could ever wish for—tall, fair, handsome, smooth—the lot. If he hadn't been the son of my fiancé, I could have fallen for him myself. No, I'm only joking. Must go, see you later.'

She returned to her typing, but the telephone interrupted her again. Jon's voice instructed her, 'Will you come in?'

She found his door ajar. 'Next time you have a purely private conversation,' he said, 'and a particularly feline one at that, would you please make sure my door is shut?'

'I thought it was. Anyway, you weren't there.'

' "Weren't" is the operative word. I came back.'

'If I had wanted you to know what I was saying, I would have told you outright and not in such a roundabout manner.'

'There are more subtle and effective ways of making a man feel a complete heel other than by telling him so to his face.' His gaze fell away from hers. 'I'm sorry that I forgot your birthday.'

'That's all right,' she answered slowly, 'I didn't expect you to remember.'

Because she turned to go out, she did not see a shadow of something very like pain pass across his face at her words.

It was after lunch and Jon was looking through some papers. Through veiled eyes, Kathryn studied his serious face with its arched expressive brows and firm, determined chin, and remembered how she used to trace his profile with her forefinger after they had made love. Her hands clenched into tight fists as she tried to control the fount of tenderness which welled up inside her body. The favours she had undertaken to ask him on behalf of her fiancé tortured her conscience. Not yet, She told herself, 'later today. Or even tomorrow.'

The telephone shrilled its way between them. He cursed under his breath. Yes? You want Miss Swale?' His eyes rested on her bent head. Who is that speaking? Max?' He handed the instrument over to her. 'Someone who calls himself Max.'

'Shall I take it here or in my room?'

'Oh, go ahead, talk to your boy-friend. Don't mind me.'

'Hallo, Max. Yes, you did disturb us.'

'You can say that again,' Jon growled, walking restlessly up and down the room.

Max's voice slipped smoothly into her ear. 'Look, sweet Stepmother, I've been told by my dad that you're interested in acquiring the services of a hero. Is that correct?'

She laughed. Quite right. The students were stumped for a tall handsome leading man for the play they're producing. Do you qualify?'

'My dearest woman, I more than qualify. I've got all they want and more. Am I being modest enough?'

Again she laughed. Well, trumpet-blowing apart, will you help them out? Who's the heroine? I am. Incidentally, they warned me there would be some kissing in it. Does that put you off?'

She became aware of an agitated movement from the other end of the room. Then the door snapped shut and there was silence.

'Put me off? My dear girl, now I know that, just try to stop me accepting the part! Look, let's meet for lunch tomorrow and

51

we'll discuss it. I'll call for you at the college. When's your lunch-hour?' She told him. 'Right, twelve-thirty on the dot. Wear some pretty clothes, and I'll take you somewhere nice. Where do you suggest?'

Jon returned noisily, and she heard his muttered exclamation, 'What, still at it?'

'Would the—would the Continental be outside your pocket? I so loved it there last night. It's spoilt me for anywhere else.'

'My sweet stepmother, since it's my birthday, the Continental it shall be. See you tomorrow.' He rang off.

'I'm sorry,' she said to Jon for the third time that day.

'Oh, don't keep apologising. It gets monotonous.'

The internal telephone rang. 'Wright here. Ah, Annette.' His eyes grew brighter. 'Yes, I tried to get you earlier. Look, sweetie, will you have dinner with me this evening? At my hotel?' He sat down and motioned Kathryn out of the room. 'Dinner at eight. I'll pick you up,' he was saying as she closed the door behind her.

Kathryn studied her face in the cloakroom mirror, applied a little more lipstick and was satisfied. Max had told her to dress up, and she hoped she hadn't let him down. She returned to her office and while she waited for the hands of the clock to move to twelve-thirty, she did some more typing.

She started at the light tap on her door and raced to open it, instead of calling out the customary 'come in'.

'You've done me proud, Step-mum,' Max told her, as he inspected the new powder-blue suit she was wearing.

'You look smart, too.' She touched the white flower in his buttonhole, and he produced from behind his back a miniature posy of sweet-smelling flowers for her.

'They're lovely, Max.'

'Give me a pin or something, and I'll fix them for you.'

She found one and he attached the flowers to her jacket.

'Before you go to lunch, Miss Swale...' The voice behind her stopped abruptly. She could not turn because Max had not finished.

'Yes, Dr. Wright?' she asked over her shoulder.

'Oh, nothing. I see you are entertaining. It can wait.'

'There you are.' Max stood back and surveyed the effect. 'Beautiful flowers to enhance a beautiful woman.'

'Er—Max, this is Dr. Wright, head of the science department. Dr. Wright, may I introduce Max Rutland, my fiancé's son?'

Jon nodded. Max said, in an excessively polite voice, 'How do you do?' and turned away.

Kathryn had the queer notion that the two men had taken an instant dislike to one another. 'That's odd,' she thought. 'It's not as if they had ever met before.'

'Er—Kathryn, if it's not a rude question in present company,' Max looked pointedly at Jon, 'but since we are lunching in celebration of my birthday, it is possible, I take it, for you to have an extended lunch-hour? I—er—asked my father's permission, which he readily gave.'

Kathryn dared not meet Jon's eyes. 'Is that all right with you, Dr. Wright?'

'By how long, may I ask?'

'Oh, half an hour or so,' Max addressed Kathryn, not Jon.

'I can hardly refuse, in the circumstances, can I?'

'No, since we merely consulted you out of courtesy,' Max answered shortly.

'That was exceedingly nice of you both.' Sarcasm curdled the words. 'Just bear in mind, Miss Swale, that I am going to a meeting later this afternoon, and that I wish, your presence permitting, to do *some* work before I go.'

As they walked along the corridor, Max erupted. 'Is that the creature you work for? I'd like to punch him on the nose. How can you let him speak to you like that? How long have you known him—ten days? You should put him in his place.'

'Oh, I—I've got used to it,' Kathryn murmured vaguely, hoping he would drop the subject.

'Miss Swale, wait a minute.' David Hickley stopped her. 'Any luck with your hero?'

'Why yes, David. May I introduce Mr. Max Rutland, son of the principal? He's an experienced amateur performer and is willing to take the part.' She turned uncertainly to the man beside her. 'That is right, Max, isn't it?'

He laughed. 'Well, sweet, the object of this pleasant exercise we are about to undertake—having lunch together—was to discuss it. But as you seem to think it a *fait accompli* . . .'

She took him seriously. 'You won't take me to lunch, now?'

He looked down at her. 'You look so like a schoolgirl who's

53

about to be done out of a treat that it would be cruelty to children to prolong your agony.' His arm went round her shoulders. 'Of course I'm taking you to lunch.'

David looked relieved. 'You'll do it, sir? You and Miss Swale together would just make our play. Wouldn't they?' He turned to his friends, who had just joined him. They agreed whole-heartedly.

One of them asked Kathryn, 'Are you two—is he your . . .?'

'No, he's not my fiancé.' She looked at him. 'Who are you, Max?'

He squeezed her shoulder and looked into her face. 'Let's just say—we're very good friends, shall we? Now that'll set you chaps talking, won't it?'

They all laughed, but their gaiety was frozen out by a voice from behind.

'Will you please excuse me? May I trouble you to move so that I might pass?'

Reluctantly, Max moved Kathryn to one side and Jon strode past them along he corridor. Max asked, 'How long was he standing there?'

'Quite a few minutes, sir. I thought you'd seen him.'

Kathryn twirled the empty champagne glass between finger and thumb, and felt unusually pleasant inside. She had enjoyed a won-derful meal, and Max had been excellent company. All her troubles seemed far away, and she had even managed to forget the shattering look Jon had given her as he had passed them in the corridor.

'Any more to drink, Kathryn?' Max smiled at her dreamy ex-pression.

She shook her head violently.

'It's my guess that you're approaching capacity. Am I right?'

She nodded slowly. 'Reached it, in fact,' she told him hap-pily.

'Now, how can we sober you up enough to greet your acid-tongued boss in precisely'—he consulted his watch—'fifteen minutes' time?' He smiled wickedly. 'Or shall we deliver to him a slightly sozzled secretary? Now that might be worth watch-ing.'

'Please, Max,' she pleaded, 'some strong coffee before I go back. He's steely-eyed enough when I'm sober. Can't begin to

54

imagine what he'd be like if I turned up a little bit,' she paused to find the right word, 'alcoholic.'

'All right, sweet, I'll take pity on you.' He signalled the waiter and Kathryn was speedily presented with a cup of strong black coffee, which almost restored her to sobriety. But not quite.

When she flung open her office door, she still felt able to take on three Jon Wrights, let alone one. She put down the giant box of chocolates which Max had given her, 'in lieu of a birthday gift', as he put it, and resisted the temptation to lift the lid and gaze at the enticing contents. She had left her escort in the entrance foyer.

'I refuse to go any farther,' he had told her, pretending to shake in alarm, 'in case I'm devoured by that wild animal of a boss of yours.'

They had arranged to meet at the first rehearsal of the play, and Kathryn was to let him know the date of it.

She tapped boldly on the head of department's door.

'So you're back at last.' He examined her flushed cheeks and shining eyes with undisguised interest. 'You're just a little bit drunk, I believe. It would appear that you enjoyed your jaunt with your future stepson.'

'It was wonderful. The food was superlative,' she warmed to her subject, 'and Max ordered champagne, because we were celebrating our combined birthdays. He said it almost made us twins, but he was glad he wasn't my brother.' She frowned. 'Can't think why. He gave me an enormous'—she heavily emphasised the word—'box of chocolates. Would you like one?'

She turned to go to her room, but he raised his hand. 'No. Come back here.' He got up, walked round his desk and leaned against it, resting on his hands. His gaze crept over her and it deepened the colour in her cheeks. 'Now that you have unburdened yourself, Miss Swale, it's my turn to lecture you. To throw your own expression back in your face, that man is a woman-eater. He's too smooth to be true, he's a line-shooter and, in my opinion, not to be trusted with the opposite sex. Although knowing your natural feminine perversity, that will probably make you even more interested in him.'

She frowned again, and felt her irritation growing as she listened. She was sure Max was none of these things. Then, still feeling a little light-headed, she broke into a brilliant smile.

'To throw back in your face the words which you used about

me to my brother, Dr. Wright, if I didn't know you hated the very ground I walked on,' she mimicked him daringly, 'I'd say you were jealous!'

With great satisfaction she watched him tighten up with incredulous fury. His hand groped about on his desk for a missile, his fingers closed on a book. As he raised it and drew it back into the throwing position, she laughed in his face and ducked out of the room.

'So you've sobered up now?' Some time later, Jon surveyed his subdued secretary who waited, notepad in hand, for his dictation.

'I'm—I'm sorry about that. As you would probably say, I'll have to learn to take my drink.'

'Not at all. With your reserve gone and your barriers down, I found you intensely interesting. However, don't let it happen again—during working hours.'

He smiled, extracted a packet of cigarettes from his pocket and proceeded to light one.

Kathryn was stunned. 'You smoke, Dr. Wright? You never used to.'

Yes, I smoke. I began a long time ago after we—broke up. Then I stopped. Now I've started again. Any objections?' his voice dared her to make any.

That's Annette's influence, Kathryn thought. Aloud she said, 'Smoking's bad for your health.'

'Well now, I'm glad to know that you still have my interests at heart.' He produced the packet again and held it out to her. 'Try one?'

'Certainly not, thanks.'

'I can't corrupt you?'

Not in that respect,' she replied, without thinking.

He pushed the packet into a drawer and raised a quizzical eyebrow. 'That sounds distinctly promising. I must try some time to corrupt you—in other respects.'

She grinned at him. 'I'm incorruptible.'

'Are you, indeed? Now that is a real challenge.' He regarded her with narrowed, assessing eyes, through the cigarette smoke. 'Judging by your past record, you are not.'

Her smile vanished. The other man again she thought miserably.

His eyes still on her, he remarked, 'Isn't it time we switched to less personal topics and did some work?'

'I'm rarin' to go, can't you see?'

'M'm. Sarcastic, too, is she?'

He dictated some letters and stubbed out his cigarette.

'That's all, Miss Swale.'

But she remained where she was. 'Dr. Wright? Is it an opportune moment to pass on to you a message from the principal?'

'It's as good as any, I suppose.' He started on another cigarette and leaned back in his chair, waiting.

She took her courage by the ears. 'The other day, Francis told me that—that it had been brought to his notice that you—we—I was crossing out the words on the letter heading about replies being addressed to the principal.'

His eyes were hard. 'Well?'

She faltered a moment, but breathed deeply and started again.

'He told me to tell you he doesn't approve of this.' She licked dry lips. 'And would you please stop.'

His eyes flared. 'And what if I don't?' She shook her head, helplessly. 'And who "drew his attention" to it? No, don't tell me, I can guess. You.'

She paled. 'Me?' She stood and faced him squarely. 'Dr. Wright, if—if your lack of trust in me as a woman,' her voice shook badly, "is affecting your trust in me as your secretary, then it's time I found another position.'

He looked at her, placed his cigarette carefully on the ashtray and came slowly round the desk. His arm curved across her shoulders. 'No, don't do that. Come on, calm down. If I was unjust, I apologise.

Because the feel of his arm around her was so sweet, because she desperately wanted to turn and hide her face against his jacket and cling to him with all her strength, she tore away and faced him with blazing eyes.

He stared at her. 'Good God, woman, don't shrink from my touch like that!'

She saw his deep anger and knew she must have imagined the note of anguish behind his words.

As he sat down again, he said with heavy sarcasm, 'I didn't notice you objecting to the principal's son when he did that.'

They were silent. Then he asked dully, 'Is there anything else?'

'Yes, there is.' She hesitated for a long time.

'Well, come on. Or,' he smiled unpleasantly, 'are you afraid?'

'Yes.'

Astonished, he looked up and saw for himself the fear in her face.

His hand went to his head. 'So much for my scientific detachment. I'm sorry. I'll try to keep my temper, but heaven knows, in all the circumstances, it's very, very difficult.'

'The principal mentioned that you're one of the organisers of a——'

'—of a conference on a certain aspect of physics which interests him. Yes, I know, would I please wangle a ticket for him? Correct?'

'Yes, but that's not all. He also wants—me to go with him.'

The words came out in a rush, and she waited for the storm to break.

'You? What the blazes do you know about it?'

She shook her head, and he saw the moistening of her eyes. He held up his hand. 'For pity's sake, don't turn on the tears again. I couldn't stand it. Anyway, I've run out of clean handkerchiefs.' This brought a watery smile to her face, which he apparently saw with relief. He looked at his watch. 'I have a meeting in thirty minutes. Leave it with me, and I'll see what I can do. All right?' His smile was almost kind. 'Now, I have twenty minutes exactly in which to read some papers relevant to said meeting, and I do not want to be disturbed under any circumstances. Not even for royalty. Got that?'

'Yes, Dr. Wright.'

He pulled a pile of papers towards him and waved her out of the room.

Ten minutes later, Kathryn's door was pushed open. Annette Linton stood there. 'I wish to see Dr. Wright. Is he in?'

'He's in, Miss Linton, but he gave me strict orders not to disturb him.'

'Oh, he wouldn't include me in that. Just tell him I'm here.'

'But I——'

Annette walked towards his room. 'Well, if you won't . . .'

Kathryn pushed herself between Annette and the door. 'I'll tell him.' She knocked and entered.

Immediately, his head came up and he shouted at her, 'You know what I said. Don't disturb me. Now get out!'

'I'm sorry, but——'

'Jon, it's me.' Annette's head appeared round the door, and she smiled at him.

'Oh, it's you, Annette. Come in and sit down.'

'My word,' she looked Kathryn up and down, 'you have a secretary like a watchdog! I had to use guerrilla tactics to over-come her resistance.'

'Yes,' said Jon vaguely, 'she's just a little too efficient at times.'

Kathryn slammed his door so hard the windows trembled in their frames. It gave her just a little satisfaction to hear his shout of anger at her deliberate act of revenge.

CHAPTER V

Kathryn sat in Francis' car and waited apprehensively for Jon. When she plucked up sufficient courage that morning to ask him the principal's third favour—to take her to view the house on his way to the education department—he had rounded on her furiously. This time there was no kindliness to soften his words.

'So it seems that once again you have been discussing my affairs with your fiancé, despite the fact that I warned you when I started this job that you must be absolutely discreet in that respect.'

She had no real defence because it had been her fault entirely. She supposed she had merited his wrath, and the doubts he had voiced yet again as to her integrity.

He swung out of the college entrance doors and threw himself into the driver's seat. 'It's time you learnt to drive,' he muttered savagely, as he took the ignition keys from her, and revved the engine into life. 'Then you could have taken yourself in this mockery of a vehicle he calls a car.'

He crashed the gears and cursed as the engine stalled. He started it again and this time they moved forward out of the car-park on to the main road. They drove to the other end of the town and when they drew up outside the education office, Jon collected his papers and, without a word to his companion, walked off.

Kathryn drooped in his absence and recalled with sweet nostalgia the day she had first met him. Margery Wright, the new typist in the solicitor's office, was a friendly girl.

'Come home with me this evening, Kath,' Margery had said. 'I'll show you the bridesmaid's dress I'm wearing for my cousin's wedding.'

Margery had persuaded her mother to let her wear it, and had paraded in front of the mirror in her bedroom. Then Kathryn had tried it on.

'It's not fair, you look better in it than I do,' Margery had pretended to be jealous. 'Come and show Mum how nice you look.'

They had gone downstairs to find Mrs. Wright.

'Look at me, I'm a fashion model,' Kathryn had boasted, walking up and down an imaginary cat-walk.

The lounge door had opened. A tall, dark-eyed, serious young man stood in the doorway and stared at the vision, apparently unable to tear his eyes away.

Margery had effected a careless introduction. 'Kathryn, meet my brother Jon. He hasn't long left Oxford University and he's a B.Sc. and he's training to be a teacher. Oh, and if you're interested, he hasn't got a girl-friend at the moment.'

'Hallo, Jon.'

'Hallo, Kathryn.' They gazed at each other and knew they were in love. It had been as simple as that. Before she had left the house, he had arranged to meet her the next evening. By the end of the week, they were engaged.

Kathryn opened her eyes as she heard Jon's brisk footsteps coming towards the car. He was still in a bad temper.

'You'll have to show me the way to this estate you want to go to. I don't know the new part of the town. I've been away a long time.'

She directed him with the aid of a street map Francis had given her. Like most building sites, the estate had a soulless, negative air. Parts of houses pushed half-heartedly upwards from the brick-strewn earth; walls, unevenly finished, had the flavour of twentieth-century ruined abbeys; full-grown houses, windowless and without doors, stared blindly across muddy, rutted tracks which would one day boast tarmac and parked cars and street lamps and children at play.

'Are you coming with me?' she asked Jon uncertainly, as he pulled in to the kerb.

'What?' he barked back. 'Look round a house which my former wife is intending to share with her second husband? What do you take me for?'

He reached over to the back seat and tugged his briefcase to the front. He pulled out a wad of papers and flipped through them. 'I trust you won't be long. I haven't got all day.'

Kathryn picked her way over the rubble and stood on the threshold of the house. Because of its unfinished state, it was almost impossible to visualise how it would look when completed. The area which was surely designated as the lounge was hardly distinguishable from the dining-room, and the space which appeared to be the foundation to the kitchen seemed impossibly small.

She looked upwards to the head of the staircase—little more than an unstable ladder—and decided to attempt the climb, but when she reached the top, discovered there was no upstairs flooring. She stepped cautiously on to a joist and started to make her way along it, but soon decided the going would be too dangerous. So she trod backwards to the staircase, and descended it warily, step by step, her hand spread out against the rough, unplastered wall for support.

She had almost reached the ground floor when her foot made precarious contact with a pile of bricks, slithered off it and turned over. There was a wrenching pain in the region of her ankle and she swayed with agony and nausea. The faintness eventually passed, and overcoming with some effort her feeling of general weakness, she tried to walk, but discovered with dismay that the foot could not bear any weight.

She managed with great self-control to hobble to the doorway, and called plaintively, 'Jon?'

He didn't stir. She tried again, louder this time. 'Jon?'

Still he didn't move. Tears threatened. 'I'm sure he's doing it on purpose,' she thought.

'Dr. Wright!'

'Yes?' He answered as if he had heard all the time. His voice was disinterested.

'I'm very sorry, but I've hurt my ankle.'

61

He got out of the car reluctantly and approached her as she leaned weakly against the door frame.

'Well, what do you want me to do?'

She was bewildered by his attitude. 'I thought perhaps if you could help me to sit down somewhere for a few minutes, it might feel better.'

But he just stood there regarding her sceptically. She thought that if she explained, he might change his attitude. 'My foot slipped off some bricks and it's obviously aggravated my old trouble.'

He frowned at this statement.

'I injured my ankle as a child and it created a permanent weakness there.'

'Really?' He smiled cynically. 'I knew you in your teens, did I not? I can't remember your ever mentioning such a thing.'

She was growing tired now and her good ankle was beginning to complain at the extra weight it had to bear.

'No, perhaps not,' she replied in a tired voice, 'but you didn't know everything about me, did you?'

'Oh, didn't I?'

She ignored the deeper meaning in his words. 'And we didn't know each other for very long, either.'

'I'll grant you that.'

He looked at the builders' rubble around the site. 'I'll see if I can find a piece of wood you can use as a stick.'

As he moved away, picking up pieces of timber and testing their lengths, she said quietly, 'Your arm would be better,' but he chose not to hear her.

She was thinking that if he did not return soon, she would sink to the ground with fatigue, but he came back at that moment and handed her some scrap timber which seemed to be exactly right to take her weight.

'Use that to get you to the car,' he threw at her callously, and walked away.

She closed her eyes to stop the overflow of tears, gritted her teeth and limped to the roadway along the sloping boards which had been thrown down haphazardly to accommodate the builders' wheelbarrows.

Without looking at her extremely awkward progress, or even putting out a hand to help, he opened the car door and watched her ease her way into the passenger seat. He took the piece of wood from her, threw it back on to the building site, got into the car and drove on.

He drew up at last in the college car-park. 'I suppose you still maintain you can't walk unaided?'

Her ankle was aching more than ever. It had started to swell and was beginning to throb. She shook her head and said, with a rueful smile, 'Afraid not.'

Jon wrongly interpreted the smile and looked at her with contempt in his eyes. 'I see you think it's a big joke. I will say this for you, though: you're an excellent actress.'

Was that what he was thinking—that she was putting on an act? Before Kathryn could decide upon a suitable retort, he had slammed out of the car and was walking away, calling over his shoulder, 'I'll tell your fiancé. It's his problem, not mine.'

Francis soon came hurrying out of the building. 'My dear, what has happened? Dr. Wright said you seemed to have sustained some sort of injury. What have you done?'

His lined face seemed very concerned as she told him how she had hurt herself. 'I shouldn't have allowed you to go on your own, but I've been so busy. You shouldn't have gone clambering about like that. Now what can we do? Dr. Wright said he could not take you home, as he has an appointment. I'm busy with a councillor. Would your brother be free, do you think?'

'He might be. If he is, he won't mind running me home. I'm afraid I wouldn't be much good at work today, Francis. I can hardly walk.'

'Of course not, my dear. And don't come back until your ankle is quite better. I think you'd better see a doctor.'

Kathryn promised that she would, and Francis went off to find Geoff. He came almost immediately.

'I had some free time, lucky for you. Is it your old trouble? How did it happen?'

On the way home, she told him, leaving out the story of Jon's lack of sympathy. Her brother helped her into the house and she lay on the couch with her ankle, which was very painful now, resting on a cushion.

Geoff telephoned the doctor. 'He'll be along as soon as he can,' he told his sister. 'I'll leave the door ajar so he can get in.'

'Look after Francis' car, won't you?' she called after him as he went out again. 'I think Jon would have wrecked it, given half the chance.'

63

Geoff laughed. 'Don't worry, I'll return the rattletrap quite safely to the Old Boy.'

Next morning, Kathryn sat in her living-room, reading the paper and waiting for her brother to take her to the local hospital. Her coat was on and her bandaged foot rested on a stool. The doctor had called the day before to examine her injury. He had applied strapping and given her some tablets to dull the pain. He told her an X-ray was advisable, although he doubted if the damage was very great, but because of her old ankle injury, a hospital visit was arranged. Geoff had been given Francis' permission to use his car to take her there.

She heard her brother's key in the lock, and called out, 'I'm in here, Geoff.' She heard him come in and folded the newspaper. 'Right on time, for once,' she commented, without looking up.

'Yes, I am, aren't I?'

Her head jerked round. 'Jon!'

'Hallo,' he said, smiling down at her.

'But I I expected Geoff.'

'Disappointed?'

'No, I mean, what are you doing here?'

'I'm taking you to the hospital.' He stood in front of her and looked at her foot. 'I'm here to apologise. I'm—sorry for my attitude yesterday. Geoff confirmed what you told me about your ankle. It was unforgivable of me to treat you like that. You must have been in some pain.'

'I certainly was. But you wouldn't have believed me if I had told you, would you?' She looked at him curiously. 'Is this a sort of penance, taking me to the hospital?'

He smiled slightly. 'You could call it that. Now, how do we get you to the car?'

'Your car?'

'Yes. Pleased?'

She nodded. She lowered her foot to the floor and tried to support herself on the injured ankle, but the slightest pressure gave pain.

'Jon, I'm afraid I'll have to borrow your arm. Do you mind?'

He studied her for a moment. 'There's only one way to do this. I'll carry you.' His arms came out and he scooped her into them. 'Put your arm round my neck, for goodness' sake, otherwise it won't work. I don't bite, you know, even at close quarters.'

She felt strangely shy in the arms of this man who, so long ago and for so short a time, had been her husband. He looked into her face and she felt his breath on her pink cheeks.

'My word, this takes me back some years. Just like old times. Still as light as a snowflake.' He dwelt on her mouth. 'I wonder if your kisses taste the same.' She turned her head away. 'Oh, you're quite safe with me, Miss Swale. I wouldn't dream of tearing down the barriers between us. I never plunder another man's territory.'

'Jon, we must go.'

He carried her to the car, which was parked in the sideway, and lowered her gently to the ground. With the same gentleness, he helped her into the front seat. Then he got in the other side and drove off.

'Your appointment is—when?'

'Eleven-fifteen.'

'Then we're in good time.'

'How are you managing at the college, Jon?'

'Not too bad.' He gave her a quick smile. 'No one's indispensable. Not even you.'

Put in my place again, she thought dismally.

The traffic was heavy and delayed their progress. They were waiting at the third set of traffic lights, when Kathryn said, 'This is a lovely car, Jon.'

'Yes, it is. I know you've been itching to try it out.'

'Who told you that?'

'Your brother. He gives away your little secrets, you know.'

She was silent, refusing his bait.

'Tell me something.' His tone was edged with cynicism. 'Now that I possess greater financial flexibility than I ever used to have—for instance, I can now afford a large car, and can stay at top-flight hotels—would you take me back as your husband?'

She knew he was not being serious. She heard the hardness in his voice and recognised the insinuation that all she was interested in nowadays was the size of a man's bank balance.

'No, don't answer that question. I don't want to know.'

He drew up in the hospital car-park and with his help she moved slowly across the forecourt to the outpatients' entrance.

'Painful?' he asked, as they reached the building, and parked.

She bit her lip and nodded. He whispered in her ear, 'If I picked you up now and carried you, it would cause quite a stir. Shall we try it?'

She gave him a brave smile. 'One look at me in there, and they'll bring me a wheelchair.'

'Cheer up,' he said, 'we're nearly there.'

He was being so sweet she wanted to cry. They were directed to the waiting-room and he led her to an empty seat. 'Sit there. I'll make some enquiries.'

He went across to the office window and told the clerk, 'I've brought a patient for an ankle X-ray.'

'I see.' The clerk handed him a printed form. 'Just get her to fill in the relevant details on this, would you, please? Can she get to the table?'

'I'll help her, thanks.'

His arm round her waist gave her firm support and she sank on to the chair next to the table. She read through the form and searched in the depths of her handbag.

He slipped his pen from his top pocket. 'Use mine.'

She looked up and smiled her thanks.

Her hand hovered over the word 'name'. She hesitated a long time.

'Your name is Wright.'

Startled, she looked at him and saw that he was frowning. 'Unless you've changed it by deed poll back to your maiden name, Swale?'

She shook her head.

'Then your name is Wright, Mrs. Kathryn Wright.'

Something inside her held her back. Still she hesitated.

'I'm sorry,' he persisted with some asperity, 'if sharing a name with me sticks in your throat, but that's what it is in the eyes of the law. Anyway,' he added, as an afterthought, 'take heart. It won't be for much longer. You'll soon be safely married, won't you?'

She flushed and proceeded to fill it in. He watched every word she wrote, then returned the form to the clerk. He helped her back to her seat, handed her a magazine and found one for himself. It seemed an interminable wait, and Kathryn was about to tell Jon to leave her there, when a nurse called out, 'Mrs. Wright?' and looked round the room enquiringly.

'Yes, here,' Jon replied for her, before Kathryn had had time to collect her wits and respond to the unaccustomed surname.

'Come this way, please, Mrs. Wright.'

Jon helped her to her feet and began to guide her across to the door. The pitying looks of the other patients unnerved her and she clung tightly to Jon's arm. The nurse quickly saw her predicament and linked her arm into Kathryn's free one. The trio then proceeded along the corridor to the X-ray room and paused outside.

'Would you like to wait in there, Mr. Wright?' The nurse indicated a small waiting room adjoining the X-ray theatre. 'Your wife shouldn't be too long.'

'There's no need for you to wait, Jon. I could go home by ambulance, couldn't I, Nurse?'

The nurse nodded, but Jon spoke curtly. 'Of course I'll wait. I wouldn't dream of leaving you.'

The nurse smiled. 'You have a very attentive husband, Mrs. Wright.' Kathryn stole a quick look at Jon, but his face was expressionless.

The radiographer was quick and efficient and it was not long before she had completed the series of X-ray pictures required by the doctor-in-charge. The nurse reappeared and helped Kathryn to a chair, promising to return soon to take her back to the waiting room. Kathryn wondered nervously how long the nurse would be and hoped Jon would not be too annoyed at the delay. She heard someone ask him whether he was a patient waiting to be attended to.

'No,' he answered. 'I'm waiting for my—my—for Mrs. Wright.'

'Oh, I believe that is the lady in there who's ready to come out. So if you would like to collect her, you could be away now.'

'Yes, of course,' Jon answered, and then he was standing in front of Kathryn, holding out his arm. 'Coming?'

She stood up, and his arm went round her waist. 'It's easier this way.' He turned to the nurse beside him. 'I take it the result will be passed on to the doctor, who will contact us at home?'

'That is correct, Mr. Wright. Your own doctor will advise you as to the treatment he wishes your wife to have.'

They were soon back at Kathryn's house. Without hesitation, Jon lifted her out of the car and carried her to the front door.

He held her while she slipped the key into the lock, and turned it. Then he carried her into the living-room and lowered her gently to the couch.

He looked down at her bright eyes. 'Now you can't say you've never been carried across the threshold. Will you be all right if I leave you? How will you get your food?'

'I'll manage somehow. I'll hobble into the kitchen.'

'You must rest your ankle, you know. What about the week-end?'

'Oh, Geoff will be here, and Helen will come over to help. Do you know Helen, Geoff's girl-friend?'

'No. A pleasure to come, no doubt.'

'Thank you, Jon, for everything.'

'Don't mention it, Miss Swale. All part of the chauffeuring service. I'll send you my bill, plus ten per cent service charge, in lieu of tip. Now, my watch tells me I must be off. I have a lunch date.'

She had to ask, although she knew she shouldn't. 'With—with Annette?'

'With Annette. Right first time. Now perhaps you understand why I'm anxious to go.'

Kathryn was desperate in case the hurt she felt should show in her face. Her smile was fixed as she thanked him again for taking her to the hospital.

He shrugged. 'I've got to live up to my reputation. You heard what the nurse called me—an attentive husband. About ten years too late.' Then he was gone.

That evening, Geoff brought Helen home. Kathryn had managed to get herself a light lunch by limping round the kitchen, holding on to cupboards and chairs, but she had to apologise to Geoff for not having his tea ready.

'That's what I've come for,' Helen told her cheerfully. 'I'll feed you both tonight. And we'll wash up, won't we, Geoff darling?'

'Yes, we will, Helen darling.' They laughed into each other's eyes, exchanged a quick kiss and disappeared into Kathryn's kitchen.

She heard a great deal of laughter and rattling of crockery, and her pleasure in their happiness was outweighed by a longing, which stirred restlessly within her, to experience such happiness herself. She had known it, of course, with Jon all those years ago. She had known the ecstasy of loving and being loved. Now the taste of the past was bitter in her mouth. Jon had Annette. She, Kathryn, had Francis. She fought off the creeping doubt which sprang upon her like a creature from the wilds, and her thoughts came out panting from the encouter.

They had their tea sitting by the fire, and when it was cleared away, Helen and Geoff joined her again. The evening passed pleasantly.

Next morning, the doctor told Geoff that his sister had sustained a bad sprain and that no bones were broken, but the old injury had aggravated the trouble, as they had suspected.

Geoff managed to get some lunch for the two of them the following day. It was Saturday and Helen had promised to come to tea and bring the food with her.

Kathryn was on the couch again, reading a magazine which Geoff had bought her, when she heard odd noises overhead. There were voices and a certain amount of scuffling, and footsteps up and down the staircase. She called to Geoff to ask him what was going on, but he didn't seem to hear.

Then there was a sound which made her bristle—a series of loud sniffles at the base of her door. A dog—it must surely be a dog. To confirm her fears, there came a short, sharp bark, followed immediately by a shushing sound. Clearly, someone was urging the animal to be quiet.

After that, Kathryn was determined to find out what was going on. She called in a loud, big-sister voice, 'Geoffrey, come in here at once!'

She heard his muffled answer, 'Coming soon, Kath.'

Ten minutes later, footsteps stopped at her living-room door. There was a whispered, 'Bye, Jon, see you later,' followed by, 'Won't be long, Geoff. I wish you luck!'

Jon? What was he doing in the house? 'Just what's going on here?' Kathryn rapped out. 'Would you be kind enough to tell me?'

Her brother took cover. 'Give me a chance, Kath. Promise not to hit the ceiling when I tell you.'

'How can I, when I don't know what you're talking about?'

'Well,' he sat on a chair near the door, sensing that he might need to make a quick exit, 'you know we have some spare rooms upstairs, the one I've decorated, a kitchen and another room?

69

Well,' he eyed her uncertainly, 'I've let them.' He cleared his throat. 'To Jon.'

'You've *what*?'

'Let them to Jon.'

'But—but that's out of the question. We can't have Jon living here. Now can we? What a ridiculous suggestion! Anyway, I haven't given my permission as part-owner of the property, and you can't do anything without that.'

'But I've done it, Kath. It's all settled and Jon's moved in. Today.'

Her voice rose shrilly. 'But he can't have!' Geoff nodded. 'You've done all this, without telling me, taking advantage of my injury, knowing I couldn't interfere...?'

'Sorry, Kath,' he was very much the younger brother now, 'but we both knew you'd make a fuss. That's why we arranged it all without telling you. He's paying a terrific rent, Kath—far more than I wanted. He said it would help us and help him, until he finds a flat of his own.'

Kathryn was bewildered. 'But I heard a dog.'

'Yes, he's got a dog. A beauty—a golden labrador. You'll love him. You know how you love dogs. He was in kennels while Jon was at the hotel, and Jon didn't like that at all. So that's how it all came about.'

'And when did you two plan this—this underhand trick? On my birthday while you were dining together at the hotel? I thought so. It was mean of you, Geoff, not to tell me. I still don't agree that he can stay.'

Geoff turned as the front door opened. 'Be quiet now, he's back.'

'I don't care. I don't want a tenant. I don't want him here. Or his dog.' She dropped her voice slightly. 'You know what Mrs. Crosbie's like about animals, Geoff. She won't work in any house where there's a pet, because of the hairs and mess they make. She'll leave, Geoff. You've got to tell him to go.'

Her brother gave up. He stood at the door and called upstairs, 'Jon, it's no good. I can't get her to agree.' He went out, leaving the door open. A few moments later she heard him say, 'Over to you, Jon. I hope you have better luck than me.'

Jon stood in the doorway, then he walked in, closed the door and looked at her. His eyes explored her from head to wriggling bare toes, and she became uncomfortably conscious of her faded

70

blue slacks and shrunken, once-white sweater. She knew he was doing it on purpose, and she wanted to curl up and crawl away from his prolonged scrutiny.

'Now, having reconnoitred the enemy, and summed up her potential,' he selected a cigarette, snapped his lighter open and drew upon the flame, 'I'll fire the first salvo.' He regarded her again. Deliberately slowly, he moved the chair Geoff had vacated, placed it next to her, sat sideways on it and draped his arm over the back.

'I understand that you are objecting to my presence in this house.'

Unnerved by his lingering inspection, she floundered and tried to collect her disordered thoughts.

'My—my chief complaint is that I was not consulted as part-owner of this house. How can I agree to letting you, of all people, live here?'

'You are referring, I assume, to my past relationship with you. But that was years ago, and no one is aware of it, surely, except us?'

She tried again. 'What I mean is, we live a very simple life. This house is not luxurious, not even particularly comfortable. We don't have central heating. We can't offer you the attention you've been used to in recent years.'

'But I've lived here before.'

'I know, but circumstances, and you, have altered since then. Your status in life has risen.'

'By that I suppose you mean I've gone up in the world, whereas you have stood still, and I should therefore consider that you and your brother are not good enough for me.'

She had no answer to that.

'You surely know that I'm not the sort to turn my back on old friends? Anyway, I'm fond of Geoff, always have been.'

She made another attempt to oppose him. 'But what about your food?' She realised with horror that her opposition was crumbling and that she was actually in the process of giving in.

'I can cook for myself. Years of necessity have taught me how.'

'Your—washing?'

'I just send the whole darned lot to the laundry. Easy.'

'Furniture? We haven't got much to offer you.'

'I have some of my own in store. A few bits and pieces collected over the years.' She found she had nothing to say. Under his relentless gaze, she was becoming powerless to counter his arguments.

He raised an eyebrow. 'Run out of objections?'

'Well, there's the dog.'

'Yes, there's the dog. You don't like dogs?'

She crossed her fingers and hoped he would believe the lie she was about to tell him. 'No.'

'Now that's a pity.' He watched her through narrowed eyes, put his cigarette to his lips and drew on it. 'A great pity. I love them. Especially mine. He's everything a woman is not—loyal, affectionate, undemanding—and above all, faithful.' He rose, stubbed out the cigarette on an ash-tray from which he first tipped out the pins, paper clips and buttons. He grinned. 'It's quite obvious you don't smoke.' Then he became serious. 'We shall just have to keep out of your way, my dog and I. Now.' He towered over her, his hands in the pockets of his brown casual trousers, his thick white cable-stitch sweater, emphasising the darkness of his eyes. 'Since I've checked out of the hotel and checked in here, since all my belongings are on the premises and since I've signed an agreement with Geoff about my tenancy—a minimum of twelve months with two months' notice on either side after that—and since that tenancy has already started, whatever you might say now, you can't throw me out. Sorry.'

He stood at the door. 'And rest assured, my dog and I will keep out of our charitable and charming and welcoming landlady's way as much as is humanly and caninely possible. But let that same landlady remember that she is also my secretary, and that I, as her boss, have the whiphand at our place of work.'

He slammed the door behind him. Kathryn lay back on the cushion. She was palpitating with fury, and only the weakness in her ankle prevented her from rushing up the stairs and throwing herself on to him and beating a mad tattoo on his arrogant chest.

CHAPTER VI

'HALLO, Kath.' Geoff came into Kathryn's room ten minutes later and handed her a cup of tea. He asked with forced cheerfulness, 'Everything settled now?'

'Yes,' she snapped, took her tea, put it on the small table beside her and returned to her magazine.

He grinned. 'That's good. Jon told me he'd talk you round. He said he usually could in the past, and didn't think he'd lost his touch over the years.'

She glared at her brother, picked up a cushion and hurled it across the room.

'Hey,' Geoff ducked out of the way, 'it's Jon you should be chucking that at, not me!'

'With the greatest of pleasure,' she hissed.

The heavy door-knocker echoed through the hall, and Geoff dived to open the front door. 'Helen darling, come in. You're just in time to save me from my sister. She's in a filthy temper.'

'Hallo, Kath.' Helen peered round the door. 'Is it safe to enter? How's the ankle?'

'Good to see you, Helen. It's getting on nicely, thanks. I should be back to normal in a few days.'

Helen handed Geoff a large shopping bag. He peered inside it. 'M'm, food. We're all starving. Is there enough here for Jon as well? He's just moved in with us.' He looked askance at his sister. 'Come into the kitchen, darling, and I'll tell you about it. By the way, would you be an angel, love, and help us make his bed? We've found some blankets and if you could start us off ...'

'That's what I've come for, Geoff, to help. Of course I'll make his bed.'

Geoff called upstairs, 'Jon, come and meet my best girl.'

'With pleasure, Geoff. Be down in a second.' Footsteps came down the stairs, then Jon's voice said, 'You weren't invited, boy. Up you go. She doesn't want you in there.'

But it was plain that the dog did not want to go back, so his master went up again and the dog scampered behind him.

Geoff stared at his sister. 'What did Jon mean, you don't want the dog in here? You know you love——'

'Sh-sh, Geoff! I can't have him in here because of Mrs. Crosbie. If she finds dog's hairs in every room, she'll leave.'

Jon came in, eyes on Helen. 'Jon, this is my girl-friend, Helen Brown. When we can afford it, we'll be getting a ring, won't we, darling?'

'Yes, Geoff darling. Hallo, Dr. Wright.'

'Let's start off on the right foot, Helen, if you'll forgive the pun. Please call me Jon.'

Jon's eyes moved to Kathryn, who looked back at him sourly. His smile was bland. 'Still working hard, I see.'

She tossed her head at him and looked at Helen. 'It's good of you to come. You're going to be a real asset as a sister-in-law.'

Geoff's arm went round Helen's waist and she gazed into his eyes. 'Am I going to be an asset as a wife, Geoff?'

'My love, you couldn't be anything else.' He dropped a kiss on her upturned lips, and they seemed to forget they were not alone.

Jon studied them for a long moment, then glanced maliciously at Kathryn. 'Watching these two love-birds persuades me that we two have missed out on something in our lives. I wonder what it feels like to be as much in love as they are?'

Helen turned to him immediately. 'Why, haven't you ever been in love, Dr. Wright, I mean Jon?'

He stroked his chin thoughtfully. 'Well, I—er—yes, I was, many years ago.'

'What happened?'

'Oh—er—the lady in question ditched me, good and proper. I've almost forgotten the whole incident now.' He glanced obliquely at Kathryn, and greatly enjoyed her distress. 'She was very young at the time,' he went on. 'Didn't know her own mind.' His amusement increased as he watched her clench her fists.

'Pity,' Helen said, safe in the circle of Geoff's arms. 'Love's wonderful. Why don't you two try it some time?'

'Helen, please!' Kathryn's shocked voice brought Helen down to earth, and she realised what she had said. Her hand flew to her mouth.

'Oh, I'm sorry, Kath, I forgot about your Francis.'

Geoff hurriedly interrupted. 'You talk too much, Helen, my

74

love. Now what about that work you've come to do?' He propelled her into the hall.

Jon edged to the door with mock-anxiety. 'I'd better get out of here fast, otherwise something a lot heavier than a cushion might come hurtling through the air at me.' He grinned provocatively and left her.

Kathryn tried to get interested in her magazine, but could not settle down. She heard the laughter and chatter of the others up-stairs, and occasionally a playful growl or a short, sharp bark. She longed with all her soul to be with them, sharing their happiness. She grew more dispirited as the evening progressed, because apart from seeing Helen, who brought in her meal, she was alone until bedtime. Helen called in to say 'goodnight' and promised to return the following evening.

Sunday passed quietly. During the morning, Francis phoned, and Kathryn told him that her ankle was a little better each day. She managed to cook the Sunday joint and Geoff offered some of it to Jon, who apparently joined him upstairs for the mid-day meal. They were so quiet, Kathryn might have been alone in the house. She guessed that they both worked during the afternoon, marking and setting homework and writing up lec-ture notes.

Kathryn slept so late next morning that she did not hear the men leave.

That evening, there was a tap at her kitchen door. 'Good evening, Miss Swale. May I come in?' he stopped in the doorway, waiting for her answer.

'Yes,' she answered with a minimum of politeness.

Jon closed the door behind him.

'Still not forgiven me for coming to live here?'

She looked at him then, and noted with a stab of conscience that her attitude seemed geniunely to be troubling him. She smiled slightly. 'I forgive you.'

'Good girl.' He watched her progress round the kitchen. 'Your ankle seems a lot better. When are you coming back to work?'

'Probably on Wednesday, when my medical certificate runs out. Why? Missing me?'

'No.' Her smile faded. 'Just missing your efficiency, which I find indispensable. Not you.'

Did he always intend to hurt? she wondered unhappily. Or

75

did he not realise that what he was saying was like a slap in the face?

'The girl who has taken your place, Jill Something, must be one of the original proverbial dumb blondes.' He looked at Kathryn's fair hair. 'Present company always excepted.'

'Jill Summers. She's a friend of mine.'

'Friend or not, she hasn't a clue. She's all right at the routine jobs, but initiative, none at all.'

Kathryn smiled smugly and opened her mouth to speak, but Jon held up his hand. 'All right, Miss Clever Swale, I know what you're going to do—remind me of my reprimand to you on my first day. You have since made me eat my words. Satisfied?'

'Very.'

'Incidentally,' he changed his position on the corner of the kitchen table, 'is there something about me which makes all young women cry? This Jill seems all the time to be on the verge of tears, just like you. Tell me why, will you?'

She turned to him agitatedly. 'You don't speak to Jill as you speak to me, surely?'

'Why not? Is there a law against it?'

She looked at him sadly. 'Oh, Jon, you don't understand. You've changed so.'

His eyes narrowed. 'Well, go on. Tell me how.'

She turned away from him, hesitated, then spoke in a voice full of emotion, 'The boy I fell in love with and married . . .' She stopped.

'Carry on,' he said quietly.

'He was sweet and compassionate and thoughtful. He—he was wonderful.'

There was silence for a long time. When he spoke, his voice was whisper-soft. 'Let's face it, Kathy, he's gone. He's gone for ever and he'll never come back. There's only me left.'

The door opened and closed behind him.

Kathryn met Jon in the hall on Wednesday morning. He was wearing his sheepskin car coat, and he was holding his briefcase.

She was still clearing away the breakfast dishes. 'Oh dear, you're early.'

'I always am.' He spoke shortly. 'Can I give you a lift? I'll wait while you get ready.'

'A lift? No, thank you.'

'There's no need to refuse as though it was something immoral I was suggesting. As you have just recovered from an ankle injury, I thought you might welcome it.'

'Oh—er—no, thank you. I'd prefer to go by bus. I always do. There's no reason why I should change now. And—and in any case, it wouldn't look right, would it?'

His eyebrows moved upwards. 'What does that mean?'

'Well, if we arrived together every morning, it—it might cause some talk. And Francis wouldn't like that.'

He lifted his shoulders. 'As you wish. I won't offer again.'

He swept out into the cold morning air, letting some of it in as he pulled the door shut.

Kathryn swung through the glass entrance doors of the technical college, and walked across the black-and-white tiled floor to the staircase. She met David Hickley on the stairs, and he told her that the first rehearsal of the play had been fixed for the following Monday.

The delay caused her to be late, and she found Jill in her office, sorting the post.

'Am I glad to see you, Kath!' Jill told her. 'I'll bow out gracefully and leave you to it. Or rather, him.' Then she put her finger to her lips. 'He's in there already. He always arrives too early.' She brought Kathryn up to date with the work and was collecting her coat and handbag, when the internal phone rang.

Kathryn lifted the receiver and before she could speak, she heard, 'Miss Swale, would you kindly delay exchanging meaningless pleasantries with your friend until coffee-time, and come into my office at once. I have work to do even if you haven't. Owing to your absence, there's a pile-up of papers. To refresh your memory, I have a class later this morning and I wish to get through the paperwork before I go.' He slammed the receiver on to its cradle.

Kathryn pulled a face.

'Started already, has he?' Jill whispered. 'Sooner you than me. I don't know how you can stand him, Kath. He's awful. I hope I don't have to work for him again. Cheerio. See you later, if you survive.'

Kathryn took her book and pencil and went into Jon's room.

'Sit down,' he said, without looking up. 'You delayed long enough coming in.'

'Jill was only getting me up to date with the work, Dr. Wright.'

'Don't answer back.'

She bit her lip. 'Here we go again,' she thought. The desire to weep welled up in her without warning, but she firmly swallowed it. She was determined not to let him get her down.

He dictated half a dozen letters, then started on a cigarette.

'Is there anything more?' She spoke in a toneless voice. She knew she would have to harden herself to his barbs again. She had, after all, had a rest from them for almost a week.

'Yes. I have a large amount of work to do in connection with this conference I'm helping to organise in Buxton. I'm wondering whether you would mind staying on in the evenings, now and then, to help me with it? You could have tea in the refectory, at my expense, of course.'

She looked up then, wondering how to answer. His keen gaze flustered her and she hesitated.

'If you don't want to, I'll quite understand. I'll find someone else.'

'Of course I'll help.' She thought she must have imagined the flash of relief in his eyes before he got up and gathered his notes together. He walked out and left her without a word of thanks, and she physically drooped as the emptiness of the room closed around her.

She pulled herself together and decided to let Francis know she was back. He was free when she called in at the office, and rose from his seat, his hands extended in welcome. 'How nice to see you back, my dear. Is your ankle better?'

'Thank you, yes, Francis.' She sat in the chair opposite him. 'I've just remembered I haven't told you about the house yet.'

He laughed. 'I wondered whether you would ever want to mention the place again after hurting yourself so badly there.'

'Well, it seemed a pleasant house, or it will be when it's finished. It would have helped, though, if we had been given the plans.'

'I'll ask George Creswell. He should know where to obtain them. You think it would suit us?'

She found she had to steady herself and keep a firm control on her deepest feelings as she answered him. 'I think it would be ideal for us. It has a lovely view across the fields at the back.'

'Then we'll certainly think about it.'

Kathryn left him and returned to her office.

That evening Kathryn cleared the table and washed up. She changed into her white-and-turquoise-striped sweater and white slacks and settled down in front of a roaring fire with her knitting.

She wished she could stop her thoughts from wandering to Jon's empty rooms upstairs. Where did he go every evening? Was he so enamoured of Annette that he couldn't keep away from her? Loneliness made her feel as restless as the dog she could hear roaming around overhead. The longing to go up and talk to him, to stroke him and play with him became almost irresistible.

Her heart leapt when she heard a key in the lock. She knew it was not Geoff, because his evening class would not have finished yet. It was of course Jon, and she heard him sprint up the stairs. He whistled to his dog, who barked excitedly as his master played with him and gave him some food.

Kathryn held her breath when she heard footsteps coming down. They stopped. There was a tap on her door.

'Are you there?'

She put down her knitting carefully and walked across the room to open the door. 'Yes?'

'May I come in?' His eyes meandered over her. As she moved back to let him in, he said, 'That outfit suits you. Makes a man want to keep looking.'

'Really? Is that all you came for? To flatter me? That in itself is unusual, of course.' She smiled up at him, hoping she could disguise the excitement she felt at his nearness.

'Your sarcasm rolls off me, Miss Swale. May I sit down?'

Without waiting for an answer, he lowered himself into the fireside chair opposite her. 'Knitting a pullover for Francis?'

'No. A sweater for myself.'

'Oh. Do you knit pullovers?'

'Yes. Why? Do you need one?'

'Yes, I do.' His voice held little-boy expectancy.

She laughed. 'Then you'll just have to get Annette to knit you one, won't you?'

He was silent. Then, 'I asked for that, didn't I?'

She counted her stitches and put down her work. 'Now I've

79

finished my row, I'm going to make a cup of tea. Like one?'

'Do you know, I'd love one.'

He followed her to the kitchen. She said, 'If you'll put the kettle on, I'll get the cups. There's the kettle, there's where you plug it in and there's the tap.'

He was amused. 'What are you trying to do?' He ran the water into the kettle. 'Retrain me for matrimony?' He plugged in and switched on.

'Why, are you thinking of getting married?' The smile on her face stopped short of her eyes.

'Perhaps. Now, who would I be thinking of marrying?' He leaned against the draining board and watched her. 'Let me see. Who are the women of my acquaintance at the moment? There's —er—Helen, but she unfortunately belongs to Geoff. There's that Jill Something-or-other. No, she's not my type. Anyway, she's scared stiff of me.' He paused.

Kathryn stood at the sink concentrating extraordinarily hard on scalding the teapot.

'There's you, isn't there?' His voice was lazy. She heard him approach, felt him press close behind her, felt his hands touch down on her shoulders. She had only to turn and their faces would brush, their eyes would probe and delve and discover secret depths.

'But we've tried it, haven't we?' His voice was a murmur. His hands moved upwards, and the butterfly touch of his finger-tips were caressing her throat. She could feel his breath moving strands of her hair. She had physically to hold herself back so that she would not turn about and throw herself into his arms.

He bent his head and his lips brushed her ear. 'But it didn't work, did it, Kathy, it didn't work.'

Of course it worked, she wanted to cry, have you forgotten the strength of our love?

'No, Jon,' she whispered, 'it didn't work.'

He moved away.

'I'll make the tea.' Her words came through trembling lips.

'To resume my short-list of potential marriage partners, there's always Annette.' His voice had returned to normal. He watched her again. 'Yes, it will of course have to be Annette.'

Her eyes were dull. 'Would you take this tray into the other room?'

His hands stayed at his sides. 'So our roles are reversed at home? You're giving me orders now. Say please, then I might do as you command.'

She regarded him like a sulky child. 'You don't say please to me at the college.'

'Why should I? You're not doing me a favour there. It's your job—to work for me. Say "please".'

'Oh, really!' Then, 'Please, Jon.'

She gave him the tray and a crushing look, but he merely smiled.

They drank their tea by the fire. Jon stretched his legs, put his hands behind his head and watched her. 'Somehow this reminds me of old times. You know, when you're not being provocative, you're very restful.'

Kathryn said nothing.

'Unlike Annette,' he went on, 'who doesn't seem to have a restful bone in her body.'

'What did you come to see me about?' she snapped. 'Not, surely, just to recite the virtues and vices of Annette.'

'Vices. Now there's a word I like, especially when applied to women.'

She raised stormy eyes and saw that he was lazily amused. 'Will you please be serious?'

They sat without speaking. He watched her nimble fingers and she watched her work. At last he said, 'I've come to ask if you would do this extra work for me tomorrow and Friday evenings.'

'Both?'

'There's rather a lot of it.' He counted on his fingers. 'Organisational details to be recorded, letters to be written, my talk to be typed in rough. Then when I've finalised it, it will have to be re-typed. In fact,' he sat forward, 'it might even require some extra evening work next week. Would you mind?'

She saw the appeal in his eyes. 'No, I don't mind. I'm free, I believe, next Tuesday and Wednesday, but on Monday, I have the first rehearsal of the play.'

He cleared his throat. 'Forgive me for mentioning the sordid matter of payment, but I would certainly not expect you to do this work for nothing.'

She flushed deeply. 'Don't insult me.'

He leaned forward and said softly, 'Why, would you do it as a labour of love?'

81

'That's right.' She looked down at her knitting. 'Unrequited love.'

He drew a sharp breath and she felt his probing gaze upon her.

'Kathy, look at me.'

But she kept her eyes hidden.

'Kathryn.' He spoke sharply.

When at last she raised her head, her impish grin roused him to fury. 'You little minx,' he breathed.

He stood up, roamed restlessly about the room. 'Do you still listen to music?'

'When I have the time.'

'Have you a record player?'

'Yes. Our old one.'

'That old thing? Does it still work?'

'Of course. I couldn't afford a new one, anyway.'

'I've got stereo equipment upstairs. You must hear it some time. Remind me to set an evening aside. Most of my evenings are spent at Annette's.'

She held up her knitting to measure it against her. She desperately wanted to hurt him as he was hurting her. 'Francis says, when we're married, he'll buy me a first-class record player.'

'How very nice of him.' His sarcasm surely proved that he was not invulnerable. 'No doubt he likes music, too?'

'I believe he does. But he was thinking mainly of me.'

He jerked a packet of cigarettes from his pocket. 'Mind if I smoke?'

'Yes.'

He ignored her remark and felt for his lighter.

'Damn. Have you any matches?'

'No.'

'All right, I'll look for them myself. There are probably some in your kitchen.'

'No, don't do that.' She found a box and held it out to him.

'Light one for me.'

'I don't approve. You shouldn't smoke.' Nevertheless she struck a match and held it out. He put his hand round hers and moved it towards his cigarette. He watched her face glow through the flame and their eyes met. Kathryn's heart leapt at the searching question in his. Then he released her hand. He sat down.

Kathryn frowned. His presence was affecting her more deeply as the minutes passed. When would he go, and stop tormenting her?

'Haven't you any work to do?' she asked.

'Why, do you want to get rid of me?'

'Yes.'

'Tactful, aren't you?' But still he did not move.

With some relief, she heard Geoff come in. As usual, he put his head round the door. 'Hallo, you two.' His surprise was evident. 'Fraternising for once?'

'Hallo, Geoff.' Jon did not turn his head. 'Makes a change from being at each other's throats.'

Geoff stood between them and looked questioningly from one to the other. 'Well, well. Just like old times.'

'Ah, but you can't make anything of it, boy. Nothing at all. Sorry to disappoint you.'

Geoff sighed. 'Oh, well, must go.' He went upstairs.

Jon rose, threw his cigarette end into the fire and stretched. 'I suppose I'd better follow suit.'

He wandered to the door.

'Jon, what's your dog's name?'

'Flop. Go on, why do I call him that? Because whenever he sits down, he flops.' He brightened. 'Want to be introduced?'

'No, thank you.'

'Oh, pity. Well, thanks for the tea.' He stood at the door. 'Goodnight, Mrs. Wright.' He turned and ran for cover.

'Goodnight, *Mister* Wright.' She slammed the door behind him.

As soon as Kathryn arrived at her office next morning, her internal telephone rang. 'Miss Smith here, principal's secretary. I have a message for Dr. Wright.' The prim voice was staccato in Kathryn's ears. The precise accent grated. 'Mr. Rutland wishes to see Dr. Wright as soon as possible, to discuss some matters with him.'

'I'll tell him, Miss Smith.'

She went into Jon's room. 'Dr. Wright, the principal wishes to see you now, for a discussion.'

'He's started early. When am I going to get my work done?'

Kathryn hesitated at his door, trying in vain to think of a suitable reply.

'Oh, all right, I'll have to go.' He pushed together a few sheets of paper and walked out.

It was nearly coffee-time when he returned. He called Kathryn into his office and flung his papers on the desk. His mood was black. 'Now perhaps I can start my work.'

Kathryn waited patiently while he shuffled the pile of letters in front of him. She realised he was not seeing any of the words. He picked up and threw down one letter after another, then stood up, walked to the window, glanced outside unseeingly and turned.

'This morning I had what might be described as a prolonged argument, to put it politely, with your fiancé.'

Kathryn's heart fell like a lift out of control. That the two men should fail to see eye-to-eye was not surprising. Their backgrounds and their outlooks were quite at variance, their ages alone put them into different generations. Their natures were such that conflict was inevitable, as neither would be prepared to concede victory whatever the point at issue.

She had already sensed in Francis a hard core which, like the stone in a fruit, was deeply embedded and unmalleable, while Jon, at centre, was as unyielding and obdurate as granite.

He was saying, 'We're just not on the same wavelength. His approach to everything is so fundamentally different from mine, it's inevitable that nine times out of ten we shall disagree. How we're going to work together, I can't even guess.'

He faced her. 'Do you honestly know what you're doing in marrying the man? What is motivating you? Is it that you're enamoured of him as a lover? Are you desirous of sharing his worldly goods, or have you simply a longing for a home of your own, after years in a Victorian fortress? Maybe it's pity which makes you willing to sacrifice the rest of your life to a man old enough to be your father?'

Kathryn could not look at him. She could not meet the eyes of the man she loved, because the probing nature of his questions forced her to face the doubts and fears which bubbled up intermittently inside her like a volcano threatening to erupt. Her silence made him aware of what he had been saying. He apologised at once.

'I should never have spoken to you like that. It's your life.

84

You've made your decision. You're an adult, old enough now to know your own mind. Please forget all I've said.'

Still she said nothing. She watched him as he rested his head on his hands, and longed to comfort him with her arms and her lips. He caught the compassion in her eyes, and seemed momentarily overcome. Then he recovered himself. 'Shall we start work?'

She ran her tongue round a dry mouth. Her voice was hoarse when she spoke. 'It—it's coffee-time now.'

He looked at his watch. 'I'm sorry. You'll have to miss it.' He glanced up suddenly. 'Do you mind?'

'Well, no, not if you——'

'Don't tell lies. Of course you mind.' He was smiling now, and relief washed over her. 'All the same, you'll have to miss it.'

He started dictating and continued for some time. He stopped at last. 'We'll leave the rest until this afternoon.'

He went out without another word and she gathered her things together and returned to her office. She sat staring unhappily out of the window. She knew that before very long she would have to face her innermost self. She would have to come to a vital decision affecting her whole future. She began typing and the words before her eyes blurred and merged and she had to stop to wipe her fallen tears from the papers on her desk. She became so immersed in her work that she didn't hear her door pushed open.

Jon was standing before her holding in his hand a steaming cup of coffee. He lowered it carefully on to her desk. 'I bribed one of the catering staff to make you a cup. Don't say I never think of you.'

'Oh, Jon!' In her gratitude she caught his hand and held it tightly. Her shining eyes seemed to dazzle him. 'How very sweet of you, Jon. How can I thank you?'

He smiled. He pressed her fingers entwined with his and looked at their clasped hands. 'This is thanks enough.' He turned abruptly and went to his room.

CHAPTER VII

KATHRYN finished her work at five o'clock. She flicked a comb through her hair and applied a little lipstick and powder. She tucked her handbag under her arm and was going out of her room when Jon appeared.

'Going to tea?'

She nodded. 'Won't be long.'

'I'll come with you.'

She was surprised. 'I'm going up to the students' refectory. It's the only place open. The staff dining-room is closed.'

'I know. I don't mind mixing with the students. Why should I?'

They took the lift to the fourth floor. They were alone in it, and Kathryn felt overwhelmed with shyness at his proximity. He looked at her and smiled what Kathryn secretly called his 'special' smile. Her heartbeats quickened.

They pushed through the swing doors of the refectory. 'It's self-service,' she explained. 'You have to take a tray.'

'You take one,' he said. 'My coffee can go on yours. That's all I want. I'll have my meal later at Annette's.'

'Do you—have it there every evening?' Kathryn tried to sound disinterested. They moved along with the queue.

'Yes. She's a good cook, as she ought to be as head of domestic science.' He smiled. 'So I just take advantage of the fact. Do you blame me, especially as I have a standing invitation to go there?'

'I suppose not.' Kathryn tried to stifle the feeling of dejection which had stolen up on her. Clever Annette. She knew all the tricks for getting her man.

'Have enough to eat for goodness' sake.' Jon eyed the meagre contents on her tray. 'It's on me, you know.'

'This is all I want, thanks. I'll have something when I get home.'

Jon carried the tray to an empty space at one of the long tables. They sat side by side.

'Very pleasant up here.' Jon half-turned in his seat and

looked round him, admiring the gay colouring of the curtains and furniture, and the modern paintings round the walls. 'Well patronised, too. I suppose some of these people are evening students. They look rather older than the daytime crowd.'

'Yes, they come straight from work, have their tea here and go to their classes.'

A group of young people approached and sat down at the table, laughing and clattering the crockery. They looked curiously at Kathryn and Jon and one of them said,

'Hallo, Miss Swale. All right for Monday?'

'Yes, David. I hadn't forgotten the rehearsal.'

'Will your leading man be coming?'

She laughed. 'Well, now you've mentioned it, I must ring Max and tell him.'

'I hope he hasn't forgotten about the play, Miss Swale. Will he keep his promise and come, do you think?'

Jon appeared to be getting restless. He found a cigarette and was as usual searching for his lighter, when David produced his.

'Use mine, sir,' Jon gladly accepted, used it and returned it. He sat with one arm over the back of his chair. He did not seem to be listening.

'Oh yes,' Kathryn went on, 'he'll be there all right. He told me I had only to call and he would come.'

'My goodness,' said a girl student who had just joined them, 'it sounds as though you've got him where you want him. Wish I could get my boy-friend to that state.'

'Hey, hold on a minute, Sue. Miss Swale's real boy-friend might be sitting next to her. Are you her fiancé, sir?'

'Who, me?' Jon barely moved his head. 'No, I'm not the man of her choice.'

David joked, 'You sound as though you're disappointed, sir.'

'Do I?' He turned towards Kathryn and regarded her narrowly. 'I assure you, nothing could be further from the truth.'

She wilted almost visibly before his eyes, which seemed to give him great satisfaction.

There was a short pause, and David went on, 'She won't tell us who the mystery man is, will you, Miss Swale?'

'No. I always like to keep people guessing.' Jon gave her a lazy, calculated look and watched her colour rise.

87

She stood up. 'It's time I was off. See you Monday, David. With my hero.'

Jon ground his cigarette in the ash-tray and followed her out. They walked along the corridor in complete silence. They turned the corner towards the stairs and Jon collided head-on with Annette. His arms went round her waist.

'Oh, Jon darling, I've been looking for you everywhere.'

'Have you, sweetie? Well, here I am.'

'Are you coming home with me tonight?'

'Of course, sweet. But I should have told you I would be later this evening. Come and wait with me in my office.'

His arm went across her shoulders and hers lifted to his waist, and they walked in a leisurely fashion along the corridor. Kathryn excused herself and, head high in the air, hurried on in front of them. She did not know that Jon watched her angry figure until it was out of sight, then removed his arm from his companion's shoulder and walked apart from her.

By the time Jon and Annette arrived in the other room, Kathryn was well into the pile of work. She heard their voices and their laughter, and tried to drown the noise with the pounding of the typewriter. When she came to a section which she did not understand, she hesitated a long time before deciding that it was imperative to ask Jon's advice.

She tapped on his door and when he called to her to enter, she saw with a shock that Annette was sitting in his chair, swaying gently from side to side, while Jon was sitting on the seat his secretary usually occupied.

'Yes, Miss Swale?' He sounded long-suffering.

'I'm sorry to interrupt, but could you please clarify this point?'

She handed him a sheet of paper, which he rested on a book on his lap. He found his pen and with it proceeded to answer her query. She was standing at his side and in order to see more clearly, bent over him. In doing so, her hair swung against his cheek and he raised his hand to hold it away from him. She knew he was getting the full benefit of the expensive perfume which Francis had given her for Christmas.

As she turned to walk away, having understood his explanation, he swung round and caught her wrist. 'By the way, did I tell you I wanted three carbon copies, plus the top copy?'

'Yes, Dr. Wright.' She smiled at him engagingly, then transferred her smile to Annette. 'I'm so sorry to have interrupted you, Miss Linton.'

Annette's cold and beautiful eyes surveyed her suspiciously.

'Don't mention it, Miss Swale. I *quite* understand.'

Jon watched them and was plainly enjoying himself.

Kathryn sat down at her typewriter, then heard a loud burst of masculine laughter. Jon's raised voice came through the door. 'If you knew how much we get on each other's nerves, you wouldn't say that.'

Kathryn clenched her fists and squeezed back the tears. She knew only too well who he was talking about.

She continued with the work for some time. There was no more noise from the next room and she had just decided that they had both gone, when Jon came in. By his attitude he seemed to be alone. Probably Annette had got fed up with waiting.

He walked across to the filing cabinet, propped himself against it and with a slow smile, said, 'My girl-friend tells me my secretary is making a dead set at me. Could she be right?'

Because her heart was breaking, and because she could not allow a single tear to trickle through into her eyes, she snapped back at him viciously, 'Me, making a dead set at you? Good heavens, no. You must be joking. I've landed a much bigger fish than you, haven't I?'

She flashed her solitaire diamond in front of him, then put it lovingly to her cheek.

His dark eyes turned black with anger and he straightened himself and walked slowly out.

Kathryn continued typing for some time after that. She heard no more from Jon and concluded that he had gone. At about half past seven, she decided to finish for the day. She took her handbag and went along to the cloakroom, and was approaching her office again, when Francis came along the corridor.

'Hallo, my dear. Still here?'

She explained that she had been working late for Dr. Wright and was just going home. Francis took her arm and walked back with her.

'Have you had a meal?' he asked.

'I had some tea earlier. I shall have a bite when I get home.'

She opened the door of her office. 'Look, my dear, why not come home with me? I can contact my housekeeper and tell her you're coming.'

Then they saw Jon. He was standing at Kathryn's desk, reading the work she had typed. He moved immediately towards his room.

The principal said, 'Dr. Wright, if you would be so kind as to wait just a moment . . .'

Jon stood still.

'Now, my dear, will you come back with me? Max will be there, but even if he had been going out, he would have cancelled his appointment and stayed in for you.' Her fiancé smiled. 'Incidentally, I have at home the plans of that house. You may like to talk them over with me.'

'Well, I would only have spent a lonely evening, so yes, I'd love to go home with you, Francis.'

'Good, that's settled. Now, while you are getting ready, I'll have a word with Dr. Wright.' He turned to Jon. 'I don't know whether my fiancée mentioned to you the question of——'

'—of getting two tickets for the conference. She did, and I've managed to reserve two places.'

'Now that's very good of you. I will of course be responsible for the fees for both of us.'

'That has been waived in this case, Mr. Rutland.'

'Oh, but I would be quite willing . . .'

'No need at all. It's a small matter, two tickets. And the hotel accommodation has been booked automatically. You can be responsible for that, if you wish.'

'But of course. Thank you for what you've done. Now,' they moved towards Jon's room, 'with regard to our conversation this morning, I have been thinking about your suggestions. I have contacted the education department and it seems that some of your ideas might be acceptable to them . . .'

Kathryn felt a great lift of her heart. Francis had not dismissed all Jon's ideas out of hand. Jon should be better pleased now, and the thought made Kathryn unduly happy.

Max opened the door to them. He looked so pleased to see Kathryn that her heart was touched. He gave her a sweeping bow and took her coat. When she apologised for having only her working clothes on, he told her she would look beautiful whatever she was wearing. They spent a happy evening together. They all studied the house plans, made suggestions and corrections.

'Anyone would think,' Kathryn said, 'that all three of us were going to live there.'

Max looked crestfallen. 'Aren't you going to invite me to stay with you?'

Kathryn glanced at Francis, then told his son that he could stay there whenever he wished. 'But it will be some months yet, won't it, Francis, before the property will be complete?' Somehow the answer to that question mattered out of all proportion.

'Oh, a good six months, if not more, my dear. Is that too long for you?'

'No, no,' she hastened to reassure him. 'Not at all. It would be foolish to hurry the builders, anyway, as they wouldn't do a good job.'

Max took her home. Francis was reluctant, at first, to let him do so, but agreed in the end. Kathryn was ridiculously glad that she had not been asked to choose. She invited Max in to meet her brother and future sister-in-law. He accepted the invitation with some pleasure.

'Did you know, Max, we now have a tenant?'

Max paused on the doorstep. 'No. Who might that be?'

'He's a—a friend of Geoff's. It's—Dr. Wright.'

'What? Your ogre of a boss? How the blazes did he manage to worm his way in here?'

'Geoff invited him. They said nothing to me until it was too late.'

'What a rotten trick! How can you stand him? First you have to put up with him at work, and now at home.'

'I—I don't see much of him, to be honest. Anyway, he's out every evening, and he won't be in yet. So do come and meet the others.'

Kathryn called up the stairs. 'Geoff, I have someone with me who's dying to meet Helen. May we come up?'

Helen's head appeared over the banisters. 'This sounds exciting. Do bring him up—it must be a "him", surely? Perhaps I can make Geoff jealous.'

They went up the stairs and into Geoff's living-room. Kathryn introduced them, and they sat down—Geoff in an armchair, whereupon Helen perched herself on his knee, while Kathryn and Max shared the couch.

Helen began in her typically frank way, 'Are you married, Mr. Rutland?'

'Max is my name, Helen. Married? Not even courting. I've got a girl-friend or two. I suppose I'll marry some day. In the meantime, I like it as I am. I think I must be waiting for a girl like you to come along!'

'Hands off my girl!' Geoff protested, and they all laughed.

Max looked at Kathryn. 'Someone like my future stepmum would do, of course. Very nicely, in fact. But there aren't many of her around.'

Helen asked, 'Is it you, Max, who's going to act in the students' play? It's going round the staff room that there's a tall, fair, handsome type joining the cast. The girls are all agog, you know.'

'Well, I'm glad to hear that my advance publicity agents have been doing their job and getting my public in the right frame of mind! I wonder if the future Mrs. Francis Rutland had anything to do with it?'

'Could be, Max. I have sung your praises to the students. They're eager to meet you.'

'Now, isn't that nice?' He moved closer to Kathryn and put his arm along the back of the couch. 'My future stepmother's getting so proud of her future stepson, she's boasting about him already.'

They all laughed again, and no one heard Geoff's door open. Jon stood there, his expression hostile. He glared at Kathryn and her companion and Max spontaneously moved his arm from the couch to Kathryn's shoulders while his free hand came over hers. Whether he did it as a protective or as a provocative gesture, Kathryn could not decide.

The contemptuous look in Jon's eyes sliced through Kathryn like a sword. What had she done to merit his scorn? Why should he look at her like that? She tried to move away from Max's arm, but he restrained her. The two men stared at each other, one coldly cynical, the other defiant and challenging.

The silent duel between them affected even Helen momentarily, then she said brightly, 'Had a pleasant evening, Jon?'

'Excellent, thank you, Helen. Annette was good company, as usual. Her cooking was superb.'

92

'Did you want me?' Geoff pushed Helen to one side and peered at Jon.

'Only to ask if you had remembered to feed my dog. With so much company around, I wondered if you'd forgotten.'

'No, it's all right, Jon,' Helen told him. 'I fed him tonight.'

Jon raised his hand. 'Many thanks. Goodnight.'

When the door closed, Max uttered a prolonged 'Whew!' He mopped his brow. 'I know of no one else who can reduce a fully grown adult like me to the stature of a small, naughty boy in one look like that man can. I'm getting out of here, Kathryn, and quick.'

'He's not that bad really, Max,' Geoff told him. 'You've caught him in a bad mood.'

'Then he must be in a permanent bad mood. I've heard him in action at the college. You should pity your poor sister, Geoff. To a certain extent, I also pity my poor father. Having him as second-in-command . . .' He shook his head. 'Come on, Stepmum.' He took Kathryn's hand and led her to the door. He whispered, 'Have a look, and see if the coast is clear.'

They all laughed again. 'It's all right, Max. I'll take care of my little boy.' She patted his hand. 'I know how to answer the ogre back.'

'You're braver than I am, then. Goodnight, everyone,' he said in a stage whisper.

They descended the stairs, Kathryn leading the way, still holding Max's hand. As they reached the hall, they heard a movement on the landing. Max looked up apprehensively.

'Come outside, Kathryn, and say goodnight to me there. It's too public down here.' And he led her into the darkness.

Ten minutes later, she returned, slid the bolt across and went towards her room. Jon stood on the landing. He spoke.

'Just a moment.'

Kathryn felt a sudden urge to run away and hide. She swung round to reach the sanctuary of her bedroom, but he called out sharply, 'I said wait.'

She was too afraid to disobey. He walked slowly down the staircase, and as she met the zero temperature of his eyes, she knew exactly what Max had been talking about. He stood, slightly above her, on the bottom step of the staircase, his hand resting on the banister end. 'I consider it timely to remind you that it's the father you are marrying, not the son, and to fall in

93

love with the wrong man would be the height of folly.' His eyes dipped below freezing. 'And to marry one man while continuing to encourage the other would be even more despicable. I know, I've experienced it myself. Remember? The years between haven't improved your moral standards.'

The insinuations which were snaking their way through his lips were so full of venom, she could find no antidote.

He took her silence as an admission of guilt, and smiled unpleasantly. 'I see my remarks have gone home. I hope they will save at least one unsuspecting man from your intrigues. I learnt the hard way, by marrying you first.'

Kathryn had heard enough. She pushed through the door into her bedroom and slammed it on him. Deliberately and slowly, she turned the noisy, rusty key in its lock. Her despair was too deep for tears. She could only walk frenziedly about the room until she had worked off her anger and persuaded herself into a calmer frame of mind.

Next morning, they could hardly bear to be in the same room. Jon called her into his office curtly and kept her there for as short a time as possible. There was no discussion, no exchange of ideas. Not a superfluous word was uttered between them. Before he went to his lunch, he called her in again.

'I shall be out at a meeting for the rest of the day. After that, I shall be out for the evening. I take it you have not decided to back out of the extra work I asked you to do for me?'

'At least leave me with some honour, Dr. Wright. I shall do it, as I promised. I do not bring personalities into my job, even if you do.'

'For that at least I must be thankful.' He walked out and left her standing there.

All her defiance drifted away. The acrimony between them wearied her beyond words. Now he was accusing her of a crime which her principles would never allow her to commit. She knew she was innocent of everything he had charged her with. She knew also that it was quite beyond her powers ever to convince him of her innocence, because he would never believe her again.

She worked later that evening. She preferred working to sitting at home nursing her regrets. She had missed her tea, because her appetite had deserted her, and even when she turned the key in her own front door, the thought of food was still unwelcome.

The house would be tidy, because it had been Mrs. Crosbie's day for cleaning. She went into the kitchen and at once saw Mrs. Crosbie's note. The key was placed on top of it, and she guessed without reading it what it contained.

'Dear Miss Swale,' the note said, 'Now there is a dog in the house, I am afraid I can't clean for you. You know my feelings about animals with hairs and mess everywhere, so you will not be surprised. I am sorry, as I liked you. I hope you will get someone else. Yours, Elsie Crosbie. P.S. I have shut the dog in the upstairs kitchen.'

Kathryn threw the note down and dived up the stairs. The kitchen was Jon's smallest room, with little ventilation and even less comfort. She forgot her quarrel with Jon, she forgot everything but the fact that a helpless animal had been confined for hours in a small space without food or water. She opened the kitchen door. Flop was lying full length under the table, looking hopeless and miserable. He waved his tail feebly, rose and stretched, then walked towards her and inspected her shoes with interest.

Kathryn bent down and cautiously stroked him. 'Hallo, Flop. We haven't met before, old chap. I like you. Do you think you'll like me?' He sniffed her, sniffed again, decided that she belonged and wagged his tail madly. Kathryn laughed aloud. He had accepted her without reserve.

She took a saucer from Jon's cupboard and filled it with milk, hoping the dog would like it. He did. She raked around for biscuits. She opened a tin of dog food and emptied it into a dish marked 'Flop'. All the while, the animal sat patiently and watchfully on his haunches, and when she placed the dish in front of him, he dived at it hungrily. At last he was satisfied. Kathryn washed and dried his dishes. She looked around and found a hairbrush which still held his golden hairs and allowed herself the luxury of brushing his shining coat.

It was bliss to be looking after him. She forgot that she was trespassing, that she had no right to be there. All the time, the dog submitted to her attentions with unconcealed delight. He licked her hand and gave her his paw, and showed all the signs of becoming devoted to his new-found friend. Now that Mrs. Crosbie had decided to leave, Kathryn experienced an odd sense of freedom. She need not keep this beautiful animal at a distance any longer.

The front door opened and immediately she panicked. Geoff was at Helen's, so she knew it must be Jon. The dog bounded down to greet him.

Could she reach Geoff's living-room before she was seen? But it was too late. 'Hallo, Flop.' Jon looked up the stairs. 'What goes on? Who's up there?'

Kathryn could neither answer nor move. She was petrified with fright. She heard Jon's mounting footsteps coming nearer. Then he was standing in front of her, and there was no mistaking his anger.

'What do you think you're doing in my kitchen? Who gave you permission to snoop around in my rooms?'

Her heart was thudding and her eyes appealed for clemency. 'Jon, I—I wasn't snooping. Please believe that. It was for Flop's sake that I came up here.'

Despite her pleading, he was not showing her one iota of mercy. In fact, he hardened perceptibly. 'Acting the prying landlady, no doubt, trying to find out what damage the dog might be doing to the furniture and fittings.'

'It wasn't that at all, Jon.' She became desperate. 'How can I convince you?'

The dog bounded to her side and started licking her hand. She bent down to stroke him and hid her face against his silky coat, perhaps thinking, subconsciously, that such an action would shield her from the angry man in front of her.

He was flabbergasted. 'I—thought—you—disliked—dogs.' Still he gazed at her. 'So it was a damned lie!'

'I had to pretend, Jon. I didn't like to explain at the time, because I didn't want to hurt your feelings,' he laughed cynically at that, 'but when you moved in, I knew our cleaning lady would object to a dog in the house. I thought if I could prevent him from going into my rooms, she might not mind so much.' She stood up and faced him. 'That's all there was to it, I swear.'

But still he did not believe her.

'Flop has been in here all day, Jon.' She knew by the hardness of his eyes that she was explaining in vain, but she would not give up hope of stirring his compassion. 'She shut him in, you see. So I found him some food and—and brushed him and——'

'You brushed him? But I brush him every day.'

'I'm sorry, I didn't know that.' She gave in, then. 'I won't trouble you or your dog again. Goodbye, Flop.' She crouched beside the animal and stroked his neck to hide her tears. 'It's been so nice knowing you.'

As she went downstairs, she heard Jon restrain the dog from following her. And he hadn't even thanked her for all she had done.

The following day was Saturday. Kathryn decided, with bitter amusement, that Jon must have muzzled his dog and locked him him up, too. She neither saw nor heard the animal all day.

Next day she decided to do some ironing. She heard a whimper at the kitchen door and a gentle snuffle at floor level. She put her iron on the stand and slipped round the ironing board with beating heart to open the door. There was Flop, looking up at her with appealing brown eyes, and she moved a fraction to let him in. His coat rubbed against her legs and she bent down to stroke him.

'Does your master know you're here?' she whispered. 'I bet he doesn't.'

The dog flopped contentedly at her feet, waiting for her to finish her work. Then she gently and secretly led him into her living-room and closed the door. She knew she shouldn't keep him, but argued that if Jon was sitting at his table working, he would not miss his dog for a while.

She sat in her armchair, and the dog lowered himself on to his haunches, putting his chin on her lap. She stroked his head and talked to him and he waved his tail in appreciation. Then he flopped on to the hearthrug and went to sleep. Kathryn found a book and slid down beside him. Now and then she stroked him. A glance at her watch told her it was time for the dog to return to his master. She was about to waken him when a shout echoed through the hall.

'Where's my dog?' Jon strode into the room. 'As I thought, he's here.' The dog raised his head, wagged his tail expressively and settled down again. Jon looked at the two of them, sitting in silent companionship. He opened his mouth to shout again, and then, as if robbed of speech, shut it. At last he snarled, 'I can't trust you with anything, can I? You're even trying to steal my dog!'

Kathryn knelt beside the animal and looked up at his master. 'It's not true. He came of his own accord.'

'And you did your damnedest to keep him from returning upstairs.'

Kathryn noticed that Geoff was standing in the doorway. She floundered about in her mind, but could find no answer to Jon's challenge. She acknowledged silently that she had done nothing to make Flop go back to his master, who now said, in triumph, 'There you are, you can't deny it.'

In a few strides, he was across the room. He seized the dog by the collar and tugged him to his feet.

'Listen, boy,' he said to the reluctant animal, 'you must not come here. Not—come—here.' The dog's tail wavered and fell. He knew by his master's tone of voice that something was wrong.

'But, Jon,' Geoff intervened, seeing the tears start into his sister's eyes, 'why? Kath loves dogs. She only pretended not to because——'

'I know, because of the cleaning woman. She told me that tale herself.'

'But it's true, Jon. And Kath was right—the woman's left.' Geoffrey insisted.

Jon could only stare from brother to sister. Then he turned on Kathryn. 'Why didn't you tell me that?'

Her eyes studied the worn patterns on the carpet. 'You hardly gave me the chance.'

'Come on, Flop.' Jon led the dog to the door. 'You're not to come down here again. I'll have to think of something to keep you upstairs.'

'But, Jon, don't you understand? Kath's crazy about dogs. She's always wanted a dog of her own, only we could never afford to buy one, let alone keep it.'

Jon looked at the brother, who was doing his best to help and protect his sister. He looked at the sister, whose face was wet with tears.

As he looked, she waved her hand helplessly at her brother, and sat down. 'It doesn't matter, Geoff. Thanks for coming to my assistance, but it's no use. I realised long ago that you can't inject feeling and compassion into a man who, like my former husband, appears to be carved out of stone.'

Jon stood perfectly still. His hand slipped from Flop's collar.

The dog went back to the rug and flopped in front of the fire. His master moved across the room.

'Kathryn?'

She raised unhappy eyes to his. 'Yes?'

'You want a dog so much?'

She shrugged drooping shoulders. 'What's the use? It doesn't matter.'

He pointed to the dog. 'He's yours. You can have him.'

He turned to walk out of the room. Kathryn stood up quickly and ran after him. 'Jon, you can't do that. You can't give your dog away. He's yours.'

'Look, I've said he's yours now.'

'But, Jon,' her hand on his arm held him back, 'you're his master, his owner.' Jon shook her hand off.

She followed him into the hall. Geoff had disappeared.

'Jon, listen to me. Let's share him. Let him be yours and mine. Then when I—when I get married, he'll be yours again.'

The appeal in her eyes must have struck a responsive chord in him at last. 'All right,' he said slowly. 'We'll share him.' He looked away. 'Until you marry. Then he reverts to my ownership.'

'Shall we shake on it, Jon?'

She held out her hand. He held it, briefly, then strode up the stairs.

Kathryn walked back to the rug, sank down beside the dog and put her cheek against his coat. 'We share you now, Flop. You belong to both of us. For a little while.'

CHAPTER VIII

After tea next day, Kathryn decided to take a quick bath. She flung her housecoat round her shoulders, carried her dress upstairs and hung it on the bathroom door. She enjoyed her bath, revelling in the scent of the highly perfumed bath cube and talc. She was temporarily at peace with the world, and oddly pleased at the thought of going out with Max, even though it was only to a rehearsal of the play. He was stimulating company and his open admiration provided the much-needed fillip for which her self-assurance was crying out at the moment, after Jon's behaviour.

She gathered her belongings together and hurried down the stairs. She put on her new turquoise slip, looked round for her dress, then remembered it was still hanging on the bathroom door. She dashed madly up the stairs, annoyed at the unnecessary delay, and as she reached the bathroom, the door opened.

'Hallo,' said Jon, eyeing her up and down. 'You look very fetching.'

She turned crimson with embarrassment. 'Jon! You're home early. I didn't expect . . .'

'Makes a nice change, doesn't it? Did you want something?'

'Yes.' She felt increasingly conscious of her lack of adequate clothing. 'I want to come in for a moment. I left something behind when I had a bath just now.'

'You left behind a delightful and very feminine perfume, which I've been enjoying. Pity I didn't come home just a little sooner, isn't it?'

She tried to ignore the wicked laughter in his eyes.

'Please, Jon, will you let me pass?' Exasperation gave an edge to her voice.

He leaned sideways against the doorway and folded his arms. He examined her minutely and appreciatively, enjoying her embarrassment. 'M'm. Superficially you've changed over the years, but fundamentally and—er—statistically, I would say not. You still have the same petite but delectable figure.'

'Will you please let me pass? I want to get my dress.'

'That pretty thing hanging on the door? Going out?'

'Yes, to the first rehearsal of the students' play. So please, Jon,' the pitch of her voice rose higher, 'let me in. Or do I have to push you?'

He settled himself into a more comfortable position. 'Now, that's no way for a secretary to speak to her boss, whatever the circumstances.'

'Jon, *please.*' Her voice was winsome, her eyes pleading.

'Not until you give me the password, *Miss* Swale.'

She looked into his mocking eyes, which ran lazily over her bare shoulders, down past her narrow waist and on to her slippered feet.

Then she realised what he meant. 'Please, *Dr. Wright.*' Twin fires of defiance blazed in her eyes.

'That's better, Miss Swale.' Slowly he straightened himself and moved a mere fraction, so that she had to push past him, feeling the roughness of his suit rubbing against her bare flesh. She knew he was watching her closely as she reached upwards to the hook on the door and lifted down her dress. She eased herself past him again and rushed down the stairs. He was laughing at her now.

But his laughter stopped when she called over her shoulder, 'Max is coming for me, and I don't want to keep him waiting. It's the rehearsal tonight.'

Max called for her in his bright red sports car. As they roared into the darkness, Kathryn hoped defiantly that Jon could hear them.

The first rehearsal was ragged. No one, except the hero and heroine, seemed to know which characters in the comedy they were supposed to be playing. The producer tried to sort out the muddle, and in the end Max, with his experience of amateur drama, went to his rescue.

By the time all the casting problems had been solved, it was too late to do much more than read through a few pages of the script.

Max took Kathryn home and when they arrived at Kathryn's house, she invited Max in, but he refused, saying he did not want to risk meeting an ogre so near to bedtime. 'It would give me a nasty nightmare,' he declared, with a convincing shiver.

They arranged that Max should spend the following Thursday evening at Kathryn's to rehearse their pieces, because Max reasoned that if the two leading players were proficient in their parts, it would help the others to establish themselves in theirs.

The house was silent when Kathryn let herself in. Not even the dog barked. It was late, and she hoped she would not meet Jon. After such a pleasant evening in Max's company, she could not bear the sight of Jon's sardonic eyes asking her silently and accusingly what she had been up to.

Jon welcomed his secretary into his office with a broad smile. 'Suitably attired this morning, Miss Swale? Ah yes, only too well clad, I see. Never mind, it will help me to keep my mind on my work. Sit down.'

There seemed to be a subtle difference about him, Kathryn decided. She could not pinpoint the change or the reason for it, but it was there. It must be Annette, she concluded. She must have got him where she wanted him, despite his protestations about being the one that always got away.

They soon finished the letters. As she rose to return to her room, he said, 'All right for overtime this evening and tomorrow, Miss Swale?' She nodded. 'Good,' he said, and dismissed her.

His pleasant mood lasted throughout the day. That evening, while Kathryn worked in her office, Jon stayed in his room. She expected that any moment he would be joined by Annette, or that he would go in search of her. But he remained alone.

When she had finished, she tapped on his door and put the typed pages on the desk in front of him. As she turned to go, he placed a restraining hand on her arm. 'Where are you going, Miss Swale?'

'Home, Dr. Wright.'

'I'll take you.'

'There's no need. I can get a bus as I usually do.'

'I'll take you.' He pushed the papers she had given him into his briefcase and told her to get her coat on. 'Unless,' he added, as an afterthought, 'you are going to your fiancé's house?'

She shook her head.

Kathryn enjoyed the sensation of travelling home in style. Jon's car was infinitely more comfortable than a jolting double-decker bus, and she told him so.

'Trying to cadge a nightly lift?'

She glanced at him with a glint in her eyes. 'It wouldn't be any good if I were, would it? After all, every evening you go to your unofficial home, don't you, not your official one.'

He sucked in a breath between his teeth like someone who had accidentally cut himself. 'Your claws need trimming, Miss Swale. They draw blood.'

The dog gave them an uproarious welcome and followed at Jon's heels as he went into Kathryn's living-room.

'Sit down, if you want to,' she told him.

He did, in her armchair. Because the fire had not been prepared for lighting, she switched on the electric convector heater and it soon warmed the room. Kathryn removed her coat and scarf and put Jon's coat, which he had thrown carelessly on to her couch, on to the banisters for him to take upstairs.

She stood for a moment looking down at him. His legs were

102

stretched out and his eyes were closed. She saw shadows and lines in his face which she had never noticed before.

'Tired, Jon?'

He opened his eyes. 'Tired? Now that's the ex-wife in you coming out. Force of habit and so on. But thanks for your concern.'

'Perhaps you're missing your girl-friend?'

He looked up and saw the provocative smile. He put out his hand, caught her waist and twitched her round on to his knee. 'For that impudence, you will sit there.'

'But I don't want to.' She struggled in vain to get away.

'That's too bad. Anyway, isn't that supposed to be a secretary's place—on her boss's knee? Besides,' he rested his head on the back of the chair, 'I need a bit of feminine sympathy.'

'Then why didn't you go to Annette's? Did she cancel her standing invitation?'

'No. I'm just playing hard to get. She's becoming too possessive. It doesn't do any harm to keep a woman dangling for a while. That much I've learned over the years.'

Kathryn tried again to get away from him, but he stopped her.

'Just how cynical can you get, Dr. Wright?'

'The vinegar of cynicism flows in my veins instead of blood, Miss Swale.'

'But cynicism can blind you to the real facts.'

'On the contrary, I would say there was something of the cynic in every good scientist. Having a trained scientific mind, I always look facts squarely in the face, however unpalatable.'

'But at least you should make sure the facts you look at are correct, before you pass judgment.'

'Granted.'

She looked at him earnestly and even pleadingly. They both knew that the real subject under discussion was unspoken, that she was silently appealing for a just, honest and impartial reassessment by him of what happened between them nearly ten years ago.

'You've condemned me, without trial, for a crime of which you have no positive proof I committed.'

'Correction. You condemned yourself to me in writing years ago. That letter you wrote to me when I was in America, about the other man you fell in love with, was surely proof enough?'

'And—and you will not change your mind, you'll never enter-tain any doubts as to the correctness of that letter and of your subsequent condemnation of me?'

'I've found no new evidence, as a result of my recent observations, to make me do so. On the contrary, all I've seen since you came back into my life has proved to me yet again how correct I was in my judgment of you. As I said the other day, history, alas, seems to be repeating itself, in an even more sordid manner. This time, thank goodness, another man is the sufferer, not my-self.' When he saw her bite her lip, he said, 'You asked for it, Miss Swale, and you've got it, straight from the shoulder, as they say.'

'But, Jon, why have you got a blind spot where I'm con-cerned? It seems that when you think about me, your rational-ity goes haywire.'

'Don't lecture me about rationality, young woman. My rational approach never varies whatever the circumstances.' He lifted his head and looked at her. 'Anyway, what are you trying to tell me—that when I see you running around with one man, while engaged to another, I shouldn't believe the evidence of my own eyes?'

'Your eyes are not wrong—it's your mind's interpretation of what you see that's at fault.' She put her hand on his shoulder. 'And anyway, even if I had committed the crime you accuse me of, is there no forgiveness in you where I'm concerned?'

His face hardened and she saw her answer there.

The front door opened. 'It's Geoff,' Kathryn said.

'Well, you'd better get off my knee, Miss Swale, or your brother will be getting the wrong ideas.' Kathryn stood up and Jon stretched lazily. 'He's always searching for a loophole in our defences, always looking for a way of bringing us together again. No go, as far as I'm concerned, I'm afraid. What about you?'

She shook her head dumbly.

'Well, at least we agree on something.' He stood up, casually selected a cigarette and held it between his fingers. 'Now, as you so dislike my smoking habits, I'd better go.'

He turned at the door. 'By the way, I'm putting on some records later. You're very welcome to come and hear them. Will you?'

'I should like to, very much '

The dog followed him out.

Kathryn made herself some tea, then she changed into white slacks and sweater. She renewed her make-up, combed her hair, and went a little nervously up the stairs. She tapped on the door of Jon's living-room, and Flop barked sharply.

'He says "come in", can't you hear?' Jon's voice came through the closed door.

Kathryn opened it and went in. 'Hallo.' Jon eyed her appreciatively. 'You've changed. For the better. Come in and make yourself at home.'

She admired Jon's furniture. She could see at a glance that the quality was good. 'You put our old things to shame,' she commented, looking round at the curtains and carpets.

'Don't sound so envious. You'll be able to indulge your own ideas when you furnish your new home in a few months.'

'Yes,' she said flatly.

'You don't sound very enthusiastic.'

'Don't I? Perhaps I keep my enthusiasms to myself.'

He gave her a brief questioning glance, then continued sorting through his LP records. 'What shall we have? You decide.'

Kathryn stood close beside him and examined the records as he took them from the rack. 'What about this one, Jon, Brahms' First Symphony? I love the exciting introduction. It's a wonderful piece of music, don't you agree?' She looked up at him enquiringly and he looked into her eyes.

'Wonderful,' he agreed absently, slowly dragged his gaze from hers and continued, 'a good choice. Tell me if I'm wrong, but didn't we queue up at the Proms to hear it soon after we were married?'

'You remember that? Yes, we couldn't afford a seat, could we, so we had to stand.' She sighed and he stole a quick look at her.

'Well, sit down. That's the most comfortable chair over there. I've put them both in the correct position between the two speakers to get the best stereophonic effect.'

He placed the record on the turntable, turned a knob and the playing arm automatically lowered itself on to the disc. He walked across the room and sat in the armchair next to her. As the commanding chords of the symphony swelled out, filling the room with impassioned music, Kathryn closed her eyes. She had never heard stereo before and the full, sensuous sound filled her whole being with delight. She was not aware of Jon's brooding eyes upon her, because she had drifted into a private world of golden harmonies which possessed her mind and body alike. She was so enthralled that she hardly stirred until the music came to an end.

'Kathryn.' Her eyelids fluttered and lifted. He was leaning over her, his hands supporting him on the arms of her chair. 'You drifted away. Were you sleeping or weeping?' He caught the glitter in her eyes. 'As I thought, tears. Why, Kathy? Happy memories?'

A half-smile flickered across her lips. 'If they were happy, they wouldn't have made me cry, would they?'

'But happy memories recalled in sadder times often give rise to tears. For that profound thought you can thank the magnificent music.' His words produced the desired smile and he straightened himself. 'Coming up?'

Her hands grasped his and he lifted her out of the chair and pulled her against him. His arms came round her and he looked into her blue eyes.

'Shall we turn back the clock, sweet?' he whispered. He stroked her hair and his cool lips brushed her cheek and her eyes and settled on her mouth.

She stiffened and he raised his head. 'I don't know what you mean.'

'Don't you, sweet? I think you do.' He kissed her again.

She became rigid in his embrace and he took his lips from hers. 'I'm sorry,' she said decisively, trying to push him away, 'but that's not my line. Try Annette, if you haven't already done so. She's a better bet.'

The light went out of his eyes. He dropped his arms and moved away. 'Forget I ever said it.'

She walked unsteadily to the door. The dog rose, stretched and followed her. Kathryn bent down and stroked him, then put her cheek against the top of his smooth head. 'Goodnight, Flop.'

'The dog is indeed favoured,' Jon said dryly. 'Unlike his master.'

She straightened herself slowly and opened the door. 'Goodnight, Jon. Thank you for letting me hear your stereo recordings. It was quite an experience.'

'Think nothing of it, Miss Swale. Any time. Do you want me to see you home?'

She laughed. 'I think I can find my way without your help. Goodnight, again.'

Kathryn caught Jon in his office before he left to take his class. 'A message for you from Miss Linton, Dr. Wright. She phoned while you were at your meeting.'

'I see. What did she want?'

'She asked if she would see you at coffee this morning. She also said this.' She handed him a slip of paper and watched his face darken as he read the words.

'Please tell Dr. Wright,' the message ran, 'that I missed him terribly last night, and that I was very lonely without him. Please ask him if I can expect him tonight.'

Irritation gripped him and he crumpled the paper and hurled it into the wastepaper basket. 'Why did you have to write it down? Couldn't you have told me verbally?'

'She insisted that I write it down. She said that it might make more impression if I put it into writing.'

'She did, did she? Then you can tell Miss Linton from me, if she phones again, that I'm too busy all day to see her, and that I'm not available this evening either. Now I'm going to my class.'

Kathryn worked uninterruptedly until coffee-time. As she went up to the staff dining-room, she realised that Annette had not phoned back. Kathryn decided, with a wicked lift of the heart, to **give her Jon's message straight away.**

Annette was sitting as usual among the men. Jim Mexby was there and Fred Welford. They hailed Kathryn as she approached them. 'What can we do for you?'

'It's Miss Linton I wanted. I've a message for her from Dr. Wright.'

'Yes, Miss Swale?' Annette's tones were icy. 'What is this important message?'

'He told me to thank you for your note but that he would be too busy all day to see you. Also he is otherwise engaged this evening.'

Kathryn felt a surge of fear at the black anger in Annette's eyes. She wanted to hide from the ferocity with which those twin brown orbs settled upon herself. 'I see. Thank you for telling me so discreetly.'

Jim Mexby threw back his head and laughed. 'Turned you

down flat, has he, Annette? I think maybe you've met your match at last, girl.'

'Giving you the brush-off, my dear,' grunted Mr. Welford. 'Unusual experience for you, Annette, isn't it?'

'Brush-off be damned,' Annette ground out. 'No man does that to me, and gets away unscathed.'

Kathryn did not see Jon again until late that afternoon.

'Did Miss Linton phone again?' he asked.

'No. But I gave her your message at the coffee break in the dining-room.'

'What, in front of all the others?'

'Yes.'

'Now that is what I would call a piece of calculated cattiness.'

Kathryn smiled reminiscently. 'The effect of the message was really something.'

'Now twitch your whiskers and wave your tail and I shall really believe you've turned into a cat.'

'Shall I tell you what she said? Then you can judge for yourself which of us was the cattier.'

'Go ahead, if it gives you any pleasure.'

'She said, "No man gives me the brush-off and gets away unscathed".'

He narrowed his eyes. 'Did she now? Thanks for telling me. We'll see about that.' He walked back to his room.

Kathryn slipped up to the refectory that afternoon without telling Jon. She had a quick cup of tea and a biscuit and was down again before he even knew she had gone. He had given her a considerable amount of work, telling her that it was the last evening he would require her help. It was later than usual when she finally finished. She had heard no sound from Jon's room and she wondered if he had gone to Annette's after all. She tapped on the door and opened it. To her surprise he was at his desk, reading. He looked up and smiled.

'Finished?' His hand came out for the pile of papers. 'You've done well. Very well, in fact. I'm indebted to you.' He pulled a chair up to the desk. 'Sit next to me while I read these through.'

The silence in the room was so intense, she could hear the tick of his large, expensive wristwatch. She hoped he could not hear the rapid thudding of her heart. Out of the corner of her eye she studied his profile, loving every part of it, from the line of his thick brown hair, which had begun to recede a little, to the dark shadows of his chin. At that moment, she knew deep despair for the happiness she had lost, for the future she had forfeited and, most of all, for the love she had thrown away.

He leaned back at last. 'Excellent.' His smile flashed warmly at her. 'Now, dare I ask it? Will you dine with me tonight? No conditions, no strings attached, just a straightforward dinner date. Yes or no?'

She hesitated. 'Well, I——'

'If you don't want to come, just say so.'

'It's not that, it's just,' she looked down at herself, 'I'm not really dressed for it.'

'Oh, is that all? I'll take you home to change, if you promise to be quick.'

'Oh, Jon, I'd love it.'

'Good.' He stood up, gathered together all his papers, and they went home.

She selected the blue suit which she had worn when Max had taken her to lunch. Over it she wore her fur-collared blue coat. She met Jon in the hall, and his eyes journeyed over her. 'You look charming. But that's nothing unusual.'

Before she could decide whether his praise was ironic or genuine, he had the front door open and was leading her out.

The dog saw them off the premises. He looked sad when his master tried to close the door on him. 'Can't take you, boy.' Jon forced him back into the hall. 'We want a table for two, not three.'

'Where are we going, Jon?' Kathryn asked him as they drove through the dark streets.

'Where do you think?'

'The Continental?'

'Where else?'

Her eyes sparkled. 'It's a lovely place. It's very nice of you to take me there.'

'Nice? What a word! I'm not nice, didn't you know? I'm taking you there because you're the best secretary I've ever had and because I am deeply indebted to you for all the extra work you've done for me. And because I enjoy your company. Enough reasons?'

She nodded, too happy to speak.

They parked the car and walked through the entrance doors into the warmth and brilliance of the hotel.

109

In the dining room a member of the restaurant staff recognised Jon.

'Good evening, sir. Nice to see you back. Do you want your old table, sir, or——'

'I should like a quiet, secluded table for two, please.'

'Certainly, sir. Would you come this way?'

They were led across the dining room into a corner with soft lighting and a half-hidden table, from which they could observe without being themselves observed.

'Excellent,' Jon remarked, as they took their places. 'Does it please you, Miss Swale?'

'Everything pleases me, Jon. I don't know why, but I'm feeling absurdly happy.'

He raised his eyes from the menu and contemplated her radiant face. 'Now I wonder why?' he murmured, half to himself. 'What would you like to eat, or is that too mundane a question to ask in your other-worldly frame of mind?'

'You choose, Jon. I'll have whatever you order.'

'You're very submissive all of a sudden. I must say it makes a pleasant change.' The waiter arrived and Jon gave their order. He asked for the wine list, which he studied with some care.

'Shall I get you drunk? I must say I rather liked the effect on you of a little too much alcohol after your last visit here. You came with your boy-friend, didn't you? Did he do it deliberately, I wonder?'

'What, get me drunk?' Kathryn smiled, recalling what Max had said about sending back to work a half-sozzled secretary.

'I thought as much.'

'He didn't really, Jon. He tried to sober me up, after a little persuasion from me.'

'That was indeed nice of him,' Jon commented drily.

The wine waiter appeared. 'A good Sauterne, please,' Jon told him.

The waiter said, 'Certainly, sir,' and went away. There was a pause, then, 'Jon, I've never asked about your family. What happened to your sister? And are your mother and father——'

'Yes, they're still around. Father's retiring soon. They live near London at the moment. Margery's been married some years. They live in Manchester. She's got three bouncing children, aged two, four and six, I think. A boy and two girls.'

'Who did she marry?'

'A chap who joined the firm as a junior solicitor, after you left. Nice chap, name of Michael.'

'I can't imagine Margery with three children.' She was unaware of the wistful note which had crept into her voice. Jon looked at her, but made no comment.

'They're lovely kids,' he went on. 'I stay there sometimes. They regard me as a sort of fairy godfather, because every time I go, I take these presents and sweets.' He fiddled with the cutlery and avoided her eyes. 'Can't resist kids.'

The long silence between them was broken at last by words which, when Kathryn had uttered them, she wished she hadn't. They were out before she could stop herself.

'Annette hates children.'

His eyebrows shot skywards. 'Oh? And I'm interested in whether Annette likes kids or not, am I?'

'You—you've been pursuing her hard enough, haven't you?'

'Have I? I thought it was the other way round. However, I shall just have to make her change her mind, won't I?'

Kathryn was silent. I asked for that, she chided herself.

Their food arrived and the harmony between them, which she had so nearly destroyed, returned. Soon the wine which Jon had ordered was placed on their table.

'Let's drink a toast to the future, shall we—our separate futures?'

He saw the light in her face flicker ominously. 'Well, it can't be to our combined futures, now, can it? Can it, Kathy?'

'To our separate futures, Jon.' And their glasses chinked together.

'Talking of separate futures,' Jon remarked as he placed his glass on the table and stared at it, 'tell me something, Kathryn. Tell my why you're going to marry Francis Rutland?'

Taken by surprise, Kathryn could only stammer, 'Because—because I'm—I'm fond of him, I suppose. And because, after all these years of uncertainty and financial struggle, I want some sort of security, which he can give me.'

'You don't—love him?'

She could not look at him. 'I told you, I'm fond of Francis.'

'They're saying at the college that your reasons are mercenary, pure and simple.'

She looked startled. 'I'm sorry to hear that. It's not true.'

'Shall I tell you why I think you're going to marry him?

111

Because he represents the father-figure you lost as a child.'

She could find no answer to that.

'Kathryn, have you told him about—me?'

'No. I told him I'm a widow and that my husband died years ago. He knows I was not married very long.'

He looked amused, not annoyed as she thought he might. 'So you killed me off. I like that!' Then he became serious. 'You know you'll have to tell him, don't you, and that legally your name is Wright?'

'You mean I'd have to sign the register in my real name and so on? I know. I'll have to tell him some time. To be honest, I've been putting it off.'

They were silent for a while. When they reached the coffee stage, Jon's hand went to his pocket. He drew out a packet wrapped in tissue.

'I have something to give you. Will you please regard this as my way of saying "thank you" to my secretary for all the extra work she has so willingly and intelligently carried out for me? And as a belated present for your birthday, which I was very sorry to have missed.'

'Oh, but, Jon ...'

'Don't spoil it by saying "you needn't have done it." Open it. I hope you like it.'

She unwrapped the packet with shaking fingers, lifted the lid of the box and gasped, 'Oh, Jon, you shouldn't have...' The sparkling brooch in the design of a miniature spray of flowers dazzled her eyes. 'But is it——?'

'Yes, it's real. They're diamonds. You'll have to insure it, won't you?'

'But it's fabulous, Jon. I'm almost speechless. How can I ever thank you?'

She stretched her hand across the table and grasped his. He looked down, covered her hand with his free one. 'In the usual fashion. Not here. In the car.'

She coloured deeply and withdrew her hand. 'Do you—mind if I put it on?'

'That's what it's for. But I'm not going to do what your boy-friend did, put it on for you. And, Kathy,' he whispered, as she pinned it to her lapel, 'how are you going to explain it to Francis?'

For a long moment, fear stalked her eyes. Then she said

defiantly, 'I'm not going to tell him. I won't even let him know I've got it.'

'What, keep it a secret from your husband? In a good marriage, there should be no such secrets between a husband and wife.' He told her quietly, 'Face up to what you are intending to do with your life, Kathryn. Think well this time before you take the irrevocable step. You must not make another mistake.'

He looked at his watch. 'Now, reluctant as I am to end this pleasant interlude, we must go.'

Jon settled the bill, and took Kathryn's arm as they walked out of the hotel and across to the car-park. She was still in a daze. This, she thought, will be something wonderful to look back on in the years to come, when Jon has gone from my life again—this time, for ever. She shivered.

'You're cold. Get in the car, and I'll switch on the heater.'

They drove home, a warm silence between them. Kathryn thought, with great relief, that he had forgotten her 'thank you'. But he had not. As they drew up in the side entrance to the house, he switched off the ignition and turned to her.

'Before you go, I want the "thank you" you promised me.'

She looked at him. He could see in the dim light of the street lamps her eyes open wide with shyness.

'Come on, I'm waiting. All night, if necessary.'

'But, Jon, I——' She stopped, stretched upwards and timidly put her lips to his cheek.

'That won't do,' he said. 'I'm not your brother. Look, I'll show you.' He took her arms, one by one, and put them round his neck. 'Keep them there.' His arms came round her waist. 'Go on.'

'Thank you, Jon, for my lovely brooch.' Slowly, her mouth approached his and two soft, warm kisses touched his mouth.

'Can't you do any better than that? Not even if I showed you how?'

She tensed and pulled away from him. 'No.'

'All right, all right. Exercising the greatest restraint, and behaving like a perfect gentleman, both very difficult for me, I'll let it go at that. But anyone would think you hadn't been kissed for years.'

'I haven't, not since you . . .'

'Not since I went away?' He was astonished. 'You don't expect me to believe that? But your fiancé——?'

She shook her head. He was shaken beyond words. 'This ridiculous conversation must end. We'd better go in.'

The dog gave them a boisterous welcome on the doormat. Kathryn turned and faced Jon. 'Thank you again for a wonderful evening and—everything.' She held out her hand.

He took it, and their eyes met. Then Kathryn felt herself being pulled slowly, gently towards him. Her left hand flew up to her brooch and she fingered it lovingly. The solitaire diamond on her engagement finger unaccountably caught his eye and dazzled him. He frowned, threw her hand down and strode up the staircase, his dog at his heels.

As he reached the top step, the telephone rang. Kathryn walked slowly across the hall to answer it.

She listened, said, 'Just a minute,' looked up at Jon. 'For you. Miss Linton.'

He was down in a flash. 'Annette? Jon here. What? Who was that?' He looked round at Kathryn's half-open door. 'That was Miss Swale. What? Never you mind who my mystery woman was. I've just got in from seeing her home, as a matter of fact.' He gave a broad smile. 'I don't have to tell you everything, sweetie. No, I'm sure you don't tell me everything either. Anyway, what have you rung for? You're in the dark? Why? You've fused all the lights? How on earth did you do that? Overloaded the circuit? But it's elementary, pet. You should never put all those things on at once. Look, give me ten minutes. Right?'

The front door slammed behind him, and his car roared away down the road. So Annette had won. She had meant what she said. He had fallen for her trick, and she had brought him to heel.

Geoff came in. 'Where's Jon off to at this time of night? Going like a madman, too.'

'Annette phoned. She's put herself in the dark—fused all her lights. Anyway, that's her story, and Jon swallowed it whole.'

Geoff gave an exclamation of disgust. 'Well, that's the last we shall see of him tonight.'

Kathryn paled. 'What do you mean by that?'

'You know very well what I mean. There's a calculated method in Annette's madness. She hasn't got her reputation for nothing.'

Kathryn felt slightly faint. So he was being sucked into the whirlpool after all. He was lost to her for ever. Her fingers groped for her brooch. Geoff's eyes followed her hand. He stared.

'Who gave you those chips of ice?'

'Jon. He took me out to dinner tonight. We've just got back. He gave me this as a gift for all the work I've been doing for him—and for my birthday.'

'But, Kath, surely it's real. It must have cost him a fortune.'

'Yes, I know.'

'But you'll have to give it back, Kath. You can't accept presents like that from one man when you're engaged to another.'

'I have accepted it. I'm keeping it. I'll just not tell Francis.'

Geoff gave her an unbelieving stare. 'You've started early, haven't you, keeping things from him?'

Kathryn felt a surge of depression. 'I'm going to bed, Geoff. I'm so tired I can hardly think.'

She was not really tired, she knew. She was shocked, she was miserable and she knew she had lost. Now she acknowledged that she had had good reason to fear Annette's angry eyes. Annette was astute enough to guess her feelings, because it takes a woman to recognise in another the signs of love, especially when they both want the same man.

She remembered, as she was preparing for bed, that Flop had not been out for his nightly walk. She dressed in slacks and sweater, put on her old winter coat and a thick scarf and called to him. She found his lead which was hanging in the hall and fixed it to his collar.

'Come along, old chap. Your master's forgotten you tonight.'

She took him for a walk, brought him back and took him upstairs, but he wouldn't stay. He followed her down. In the end, she gave in. She carried his basket and his blankets into her bedroom, put them into a corner and he curled up and settled down at once.

'You must have been lonely, Flop. Like me.'

Despite her unhappiness she fell asleep straight away. There was a noise in the hall. The front door opened and closed. Kathryn switched on her torch and looked at her watch. Nearly two o'clock. It was late, but Jon was home. He had come home. Kathryn was wide awake now. She listened to the soft footsteps which went upstairs, then came down again. They stopped outside her bedroom door. Kathryn heard a gentle tap and Flop gave a short bark. Kathryn did not stir. The footsteps went away. Now Jon knew where his dog was sleeping.

CHAPTER IX

KATHRYN found Jon standing at her desk when she arrived next morning. He was reading a letter.

'Sorry I'm late,' she said, hanging up her coat and scarf. 'I missed the bus.'

'That's all right,' he murmured, without looking up. 'Just say the word and I'll give you a lift. Every morning.' He moved towards his room. 'Come in when you're ready, will you?'

His smile did something to Kathryn's heart. She smiled back.

'Incidentally, Kathryn, thanks for looking after my—our dog.'

She laughed. 'He wouldn't sleep in his usual place.'

'I don't blame him. What creature in his right mind would, if he had the chance of sleeping where Flop did! Did you hear me come in? It was very late.'

'Yes. Flop barked when you tapped on my door.'

'You heard me and you didn't let me in?' His voice held mock-indignation.

'I told you, I'm not the sort to ...'

'All right, Miss Swale, I've got the message by now. If you say it often enough, I might even begin to believe it.'

Her external telephone rang and she lifted the receiver.

'Yes, Miss Swale here. It's who? Oh, hallo, Max. Yes, to-night, at my place. About seven-thirty or eight.' Kathryn heard Jon moving about in his room. His door was still open, and she wished he would shut it. 'Will you want some food, Max, or will you have your meal first? Right, no food. Coffee later, then, when we've done some work!' She lowered her voice. 'What? Yes, he's in his office. No, my head's still intact, but he'll bite it off for sure if I don't go now. 'Bye. See you this evening.' She hoped Jon had not heard her final words.

When she went in to him, ready for work, he looked at her narrowly, but said nothing. He read through the papers in front

116

of him, and when he spoke his voice was back to normal, no softness, no friendliness.

'Perhaps we can get on, now that you've finalised your evening arrangements.' He was curt, his eyes granite-hard.

'I'm sorry.'

He began dictating, and was in the middle of a letter when the internal telephone cut across his words. Kathryn dived across his desk to answer it. At exactly the same time, Jon reached out and their hands clasped on the receiver. Their eyes did battle, Jon's conquered, and Kathryn withdrew her hand.

'At least our reactions are in complete sympathy, if nothing else,' he said, a mocking glint in his eye. 'Yes?' into the receiver. Without a word, he handed it to her.

'Miss Swale here. Yes, Francis. Yes, Max is coming tonight to my house. I've got Saturday free, Francis. Shall I come to you? You'd rather come to me? That would be nice. About eightish? Fine. Yes,' she stole a quick look at Jon, who was frowning out of the window, and jingling the keys in his pocket, 'we were in the middle of a letter. Goodbye now, Francis.'

'I'm terribly sorry,' she said softly.

'Oh, don't apologise. But it's a good thing there are only two of them in the family, otherwise we might as well give up until they'd all taken it in turn to phone you to arrange their respective dates.'

Kathryn managed to suppress a smile and they settled down to work once more.

Geoff was home early that evening, and they had tea by the fire in Kathryn's room. She cleared away as soon as they had finished.

Geoff noticed her haste. 'What's the hurry? Got a date with the Old Boy?'

'No. With his son.'

'Max? Look here, Kath, what sort of game do you think you're playing? Who exactly are you marrying—father or son?'

'Don't you start, Geoff. That's Jon's line. Has he been talking to you?'

'Well, he——'

'He has. I can recognise the symptoms. I assure you, Geoff, there's nothing between Max and myself. We're simply going to rehearse our parts.'

117

'You might think you are, but he may have other ideas. He's a smooth character. A bit too smooth, if you ask me.'

'I'm not asking you.' She looked pointedly at the clock on the mantelpiece. 'Sorry to turn you out, but it's time you went.' Her brother did as he was told.

She changed into a white roll-necked sweater and blue wool skirt. She wore a long pendant round her neck, and a matching bracelet on her slim wrist.

She welcomed Max with her sweetest smile. 'Come in. Nice to see you.'

'M'm.' He looked her up and down. 'Nice to see you looking nice.' He stared upwards to the landing and his face registered imitation fear. 'Are we alone, or is my pet hate at home?'

'If you mean my boss, no, he goes out every evening to his girl-friend's place. You can relax. There's only Geoff up there. And the dog, of course.'

She took his coat and hung it in the hall cupboard. She looked at the small black case in his hand. 'What's that?' she asked as she showed him into the living room.

'Tell you in a minute.' He put it on the table and moved across to the hearth, rubbing his hands appreciatively in front of the roaring fire. 'Central heating may be the in thing,' he commented, staring into the leaping flames, 'but there's something heart-warming about a good old-fashioned open fire which no amount of characterless radiators or warm air vents can give you.' He turned to her. 'By the way, how's the house going?'

'I don't know. I'll be discussing it with your father when he comes here on Saturday evening.' Her interest in the little black case revived and she touched it. 'Tell me what this thing is, Max.'

'That, beautiful?' He smiled at her. 'It's a portable tape recorder. Ever heard your voice talking back at you?'

'Can't say I have. Why?'

'You'll get a shock when you do. You may not even like it!'

'Why did you bring it?'

'The idea is to rehearse our pieces, record them, then play them back. Thus we can hear ourselves and criticise our performances in a detached kind of way. All the best actors and actresses do it.'

'That sounds fun. When can we start?'

'Eager and willing? That's what I like to hear.'

'Now, Max, behave yourself. Have you brought your copy of the play? Then let's get on with it.'

'When I've set the recorder going.' He removed the case, and put a cassette into position. 'When I press this button, we're being recorded. Right?'

Kathryn enjoyed herself. Max was such a good actor that his skill carried her along with him, and she felt her performance rising to his high standard. When he played their voices back on the tape recorder, they were pleased with the result. They repeated the whole thing two or three times, and at each playback they listened critically, improving on their performances every time. Then they put away their books and spoke it through again from memory.

'That's enough for one evening, partner.' He glanced at Kathryn, and with a smile said, 'Listen.' He pressed a button on the tape recorder and their voices emerged at such a high speed that they sounded like chattering monkeys. He turned the volume up until the sound filled the room.

Kathryn burst into laughter, and Max smiled at her amusement. He stopped it, and she urged, 'Do it again, Max. It's so funny,' and he did it again. She doubled up with laughter once more.

Max said, 'You're just a kid at heart, aren't you?' He stood up, caught her by the hands. 'Come on, beautiful, let's practise the embrace.' He was in the act of pulling her forcibly to her feet, when the door burst open. Jon stood there, his expression vitriolic.

'I'm so sorry to interrupt,' his sarcasm burnt like acid, 'but I do happen to be working overhead. The noise you're generating makes coherent thought virtually impossible. I should appreciate it greatly if you would turn the volume down and reduce the noise level by several decibels.' The look he gave Kathryn chilled her to the heart. He closed the door behind him.

Max's eyes burned with rage, and his voice was unnecessarily loud. 'What about that kiss, beautiful?' His arms went to her waist and he pulled her against him.

She jerked away. 'Not now, Max, please. I'm not in the mood.' Her eyes were weary, her body sagged under the weight of despair.

'What I couldn't do to that nasty piece of work,' Max hissed. 'Who the blazes does he think he is?'

119

'Calm down, Max. I'll make some coffee. I could do with some.'

'You can say that again!'

The coffee eased them both into a calmer frame of mind. They sat side by side on the couch and talked.

'Max, tell me something about your mother.' Kathryn looked into his face. 'Or does it upset you to talk about her?'

'My mother? Oh, she was sweet, kindly, thoughtful. Couldn't have been better as a mother. As a wife—well, I realised as I grew up that she was too sweet. She spoilt my father. She was at his beck and call, she did everything to please him, and he takes some pleasing. She made him what he is now, a difficult man, pedantic, impossible at times. I suppose that side of his nature hasn't come through to you yet? No doubt he's keeping it under lock and key. But be warned, dear girl, that is the role he will cast you in—the submissive, uncritical wife.'

'You're speaking so frankly, Max. How can you talk about your father so dispassionately? Aren't you fond of him?'

'Yes, I'm fond of the old man, but if you hadn't wanted the truth, Kathryn, you should have told me.' He turned to her. 'Now tell me something about yourself. How is it that an attractive young woman like you has escaped the clutches of a man for such a long time?'

'Me, Max? Well, since it seems to be a time for confidences, I've been married before. Didn't you know?'

He looked staggered. 'You could have fooled me. Does Dad know?'

'I told him I was a——' She stopped, took a breath and continued. 'He thinks I'm a widow.' She stared into the fire. 'But I'm not, Max. I divorced my husband. For desertion.'

'Whew!' He looked quite concerned. 'Do you happen to know my father's views on divorce?'

'No.' The word was a whisper.

'Well, he's dead against it. Absolutely resolute on the subject. Nothing religious about it—purely personal conviction on his part. You've got a problem there, beautiful, a real problem.' He rose, pulled down his pullover, buttoned his jacket. 'My advice to you is not to delay too long telling the old man. He might forgive you at this stage. If you left it too late to tell him, he could make your life hell after you're married to him.'

'The worst part is, Max, that our mutual friends, the Creswells—you know Mr. Creswell is a solicitor—introduced us. And Mr. Creswell acted for me throughout the divorce proceedings. He knows all about me.'

'You are on a knife-edge, good and proper, Miss Kathryn Swale.' He touched her cheek. 'Come to think of it, that's not your real name, is it? Who are you, Mrs.—what?'

'Sorry, Max, it's a closely guarded secret.'

'Is it, now? Curiouser and curiouser. See me out, beautiful?' He shrugged into his coat and they stood in the hall. 'May I kiss you goodnight, Kathryn?'

Slowly, she turned her cheek towards him. 'Just a small peck, Stepson.'

He looked down at her, and his expression changed. 'Stepson be damned!' She was seized by the shoulders and pulled roughly to him. His kiss on her soft mouth was swift, hard and thorough. Then he repeated it.

'Goodnight, sweet Kathryn.' She staggered back and he laughed softly.

Her face was pale, she appeared to be deeply shocked.

'Don't take it so hard, beautiful. You'll have to do better than that on the night. Never mind, practice makes perfect.'

'You shouldn't have done that, Max,' she whispered, but he merely laughed again, flicked his eyes to the upstairs landing with an odd smile of triumph, and was gone.

'You shouldn't have asked for it.' She swung round, and saw Jon standing on the stairs. So that was why Max had done it! She clenched her fists.

'It's no concern of yours what I do with my private life.'

'Private? Since when has an entrance hall been private?' He walked downstairs. 'And perhaps I should remind you—although with your experience of men, you should know—that when a woman plays with fire, it's usually her fingers which get burnt, not the man's.'

'Why should you worry about my burnt fingers? You're not my guardian. I'm nothing to you now.'

'That's a statement I wouldn't dream of disputing. But I don't like to see a woman—any woman—making a complete fool of herself as you're doing.'

Kathryn recoiled at the infinite contempt in his eyes.

'And you had the audacity to play Little Miss Innocent in my car last night, all big-eyed, modest and shy. I thought my

121

defences were impregnable where you were concerned, but, my God, I was nearly taken in by you for a second time. I forgot, of course, the vital factor—that your hobby is acting, and act you did. Most convincingly.'

Geoff, who had appeared on the landing, seemed very agitated.

'But, Jon, you don't understand. Kath isn't like that——'

His sister snapped at him, 'Keep out of this, Geoffrey. Nothing you can say to this man will make any difference. Where I'm concerned, he's wilfully deaf and blind. You may not realise it,' she was still addressing her brother, 'but what we are now being presented with are the results of a piece of ruthless, soulless scientific research which Dr. Wright has been conducting into my behaviour with the opposite sex. What he can't seem to realise,' her voice faltered and steadied, 'is that a scientist who sees only with his mind and never with his heart is no more human than the scientific equipment he works with. If a scientist cannot combine his cool detachment with compassion and humanity,' she was breathing hard and struggling to hold back her tears, 'then he is no more than a highly skilled robot.' She fixed her eyes on Jon. 'Which just about sums up Dr. Jon Wright.' She slammed her door in his face.

His attitude towards her next day was as deeply cold as Arctic ice. She could do nothing right for him. His criticisms stung her to tears which, now and then, she had to let fall. But he merely watched and waited while she took out her handkerchief and wiped them off the notebook she was using. She thought the day would never end.

During the afternoon, he took a phone call from Annette. He put his hand over the mouthpiece and said curtly to Kathryn, 'Please return to your room while I speak to Miss Linton.'

She heard him say, 'About eightish tomorrow evening, sweetie. You'll bring the food? Wonderful. I can provide most of the crockery, and of course the drink. I'll pick you up and take you back to my place. All right?'

'It sounds like a party,' Kathryn thought miserably, as she gazed out of the window and waited for him to finish his conversation. She wondered if Geoff had been invited. Then he called her back into his office and they proceeded with their work.

122

She got away from the college early that day. She had an evening of cleaning in front of her, so she had her tea quickly and put Geoff's into the oven to keep warm. She changed into slacks and long-sleeved jumper and carried the vacuum cleaner upstairs.

Flop welcomed her with delight, sniffing at the nozzle and hose of the cleaner and generally getting in the way. She pushed him aside gently and started on Geoff's living-room.

She hesitated outside Jon's rooms. If she went in, would he accuse her of snooping again? She decided to risk it and tackled the kitchen first. When she had finished, she felt that even Mrs. Crosbie could not have done better.

She looked at his living-room. 'If he's giving a party tomorrow,' she argued, 'it will have to be cleaned.' So cleaned it was, and dusted and tidied.

His bedroom? She stood outside it for a long time. Should she go in? She pushed the door open. The bed had been made, but clothes were everywhere. She was undecided for only a few seconds, then, her feminine instincts thoroughly aroused, she went to work with a will.

She folded his clothes, and pushed them into a drawer. She hung his jackets in the wardrobe, and put his shoes in a neat row under the bed. As she touched his belongings, she threw off the treacherous longing which crept up on her like an enemy unseen.

She started cleaning the carpet, and was so deafened by the noise of the vacuum cleaner and so absorbed in her work that she did not see Jon open the door, stare at her antics and lower himself, smiling, on to his bed. When at last she saw him sitting there, she had a thorough shock.

He was leaning nonchalantly against the wall, his head supported on the linked palms of his upraised hands. His bland expression annoyed her, as he watched her moving the cleaner rhythmically over the carpet.

At last she switched off and looked at him. 'I hope you don't mind my being in here, but it's only what a domestic help would do.'

'Oh, don't apologise. I find it soothing to watch you work.' His grin infuriated her. 'Before you start again, tell me something.' He looked around. 'Surely this is the room we shared when we lived together?' His choice of words was deliberate,

123

Kathryn was sure. 'Only the bed wasn't here, it was in the centre, and the furniture was arranged somewhat differently? Isn't that so?'

'You're quite right.' she answered dully.

'M'm. No wonder this room holds such interesting memories.' His eyes became dreamy and he studied her reaction. She coloured and bent down to switch on the cleaner again, but he stopped her. 'Before you start again, are you any good at sewing?'

'I have to be out of necessity. Why?' She looked at him suspiciously, and saw him finger the edge of his jacket.

'Geoff tells me you sew on his buttons. Can I persuade you to do likewise to mine?'

'How did you manage in the past?' She knew she sounded sulky.

'Oh,' he answered airily, 'there was always a willing girl-friend around.'

'You have a willing girl-friend now, haven't you? Why can't you ask her?'

'Because I'm asking you, that's why. Well, what's the answer?'

She nodded, and switched on the cleaner again.

She felt his eyes clinging to her every movement, and when she straightened up from cleaning under the furniture and switched off again, his next words shook her to the core.

'Do you know,' his voice drawled, 'you've grown more beautiful with time than I would ever have believed possible?'

She dropped the cleaner handle in the confusion wrought inside her at his words. He was obviously baiting her, because he now smiled maliciously.

'And it's all going to be wasted on an old man. I should never have let you go, should I? I should have fought harder against this "someone else" you took up with in my absence. Tell me, was he handsome, this man, did you love him as passionately as you once loved me?'

As she opened her mouth to reply, he held up his hand. 'No, on second thoughts, don't tell me. No man wants to hear the intimate details of his rival. You know, I was a fool. I should have known better than to let you go. I would then have enjoyed your—company a little longer, if not your genuine love. After all, one can always'—he paused, and allowed his gaze to

124

wander over her—'enjoy a beautiful woman, even though love isn't there to lend it sweetness and spice.'

The colour which flooded her face at his words seemed to give him immense satisfaction, and she jerked the plug from the socket and pulled the cleaner out of his room. She banged his door, only to find that it was immediately opened again.

He was holding out his jacket. 'Please?'

She hesitated, snatched it from him and threw it across the banisters. 'The button's in the inside pocket, you sweet-tempered little woman.' Then he shut the door on her.

Later that evening, she sewed on the button. As she turned the jacket into a more convenient position, the contents of his pockets fell out on to the carpet. She picked up the bits and pieces and stuffed them back. His wallet was lying on the floor and underneath it was an envelope. She picked it up with trembling fingers. She could not believe her eyes—she was looking at her own handwriting. She saw from the date on the postmark that the letter was nearly ten years old. It was addressed to him in America, and it was one of the first she had written after his departure from England.

The impulse to read it was too strong to resist. As her eyes took in the words, her face flamed. It was a passionate love letter, written from the depths of her heart, which had seemed at the time to be breaking with loneliness and despair and longing for his return. Even now the memories it evoked brought tears to her eyes. She was sharing once again the hopelessness and misery expressed so movingly by the young girl who had written those words so long ago.

She pushed it back into his pocket and carried the jacket upstairs. She tapped on his door and he turned as she went in. He was sitting at the table working, and the dog was at his feet.

'My jacket?' He held out his hand. 'Thanks for mending it.'

That was all he said.

'I'm sorry, but as I turned it round everything fell out. There—there was a letter . . .'

'What letter?'

'It was an old letter, from me, written to you in America . . .'

'Oh, that one. Have I still got it? It's no good now, is it?' He rooted around in his pocket, found it and inspected the en-

125

velope. 'Might as well chuck it away.' He looked at her as she stood at his side. 'Unless you want it?'

She put her hands behind her back as though it was something unpleasant he was offering her. 'No, thank you. It's yours.'

He shrugged his shoulders. 'Well, since neither of us wants it——' He aimed at the waste-paper basket and it went straight in. He dusted his hands and got on with his work.

Still she stood there, her lips trembling, dismay robbing her of words. She felt as though he had torn her heart from her body and thrown it on the rubbish heap.

'Was there anything else? I've thanked you for doing the job, haven't I?' He looked up at her long-sufferingly.

The tears spilled over, then. 'You—you're a miserable, heartless brute!' she sobbed, and ran from the room.

'Geoff, have you been invited to Jon's party?' she asked her brother next morning.

'Yes. And Helen. Haven't you?'

'No. I only knew about it because he discussed it with Annette on the phone yesterday.'

Her brother seemed upset. 'I would have thought he'd have asked you, Kath.'

'I wouldn't have been able to go, anyway. Francis is coming this evening. Jon knew that because he heard me making the arrangements. Who else is going, Geoff?'

'Some friends of his, in the firm he used to work for, and their wives or girl-friends as the case may be. There'll be at least a dozen of us, probably more. Do you mind, Kath, if we borrow some of your crockery?'

She was about to refuse but she shrugged her shoulders instead. What was the use? 'As long as you leave me with enough for my own purposes, you can have my crockery.'

She did not see Jon until the early evening, when she was leaving the bathroom, wearing her housecoat. He was coming out of his kitchen. 'Hallo,' he said.

She didn't answer.

'Aren't we on speaking terms now?'

'No.'

'Well, at least I've got one word out of you.'

She swept past him and down the stairs. She dressed carefully for Francis' visit, built up a roaring fire with logs and did her utmost to persuade herself into a more welcoming frame of mind. Instead of entertaining her fiancé, she wanted desperately to run and hide and cry her heart out—for another man.

As the time drew near to Francis' arrival, her tension increased. A car pulled up outside and at the same time there was a loud knock on the front door. Thinking it was Francis, she went to open it. Standing there, talking and laughing, was a group of people who had come for the party. They were friendly, assumed she was also a guest, and started joking with her about the weather. When Jon came down to greet them, looking handsome and happy, he ignored Kathryn completely. She might not have existed.

Then Francis appeared on the doorstep. He seemed a little bewildered by all the noise and bustle. He saw Jon, wished him a polite good evening, and followed Kathryn into her living-room.

She knew Jon's guests had watched her welcome Francis, and they seemed a little surprised, not to say disappointed, when she did not join them on their way upstairs.

'Who's she?' she heard one of the men say to Jon.

Jon looked over his shoulder. His reply was off-hand. 'Her? Oh, she's just my landlady.' At which there was a burst of loud laughter.

Kathryn's teeth caught her lip, then, with a great effort, she gave all her attention to her fiancé. 'Did I tell you, Francis, that Dr. Wright was a tenant of ours?'

'I'm not sure whether you told me, but I know Max did.'

Kathryn wondered what else Max had told his father about their tenant. She joined Francis on the couch.

Her fiancé went on, 'I believe you said that Dr. Wright was an old friend of your brother's. Is there any particular reason why he is living here?'

'Tell him now,' her conscience cried out inside her. 'Tell him about Jon. What better time than now?' She did violent battle with that conscience and it slunk away defeated.

'He—he wanted to move out of the hotel because he has a dog. I don't think he intends to remain here. He's looking for a flat.'

'Dr. Wright speaks well of you. He told me he thought you were wasted as a secretary, and suggested that after we were married, you might like to attend evening classes at the college, and study for some better qualifications. Would the idea appeal to you?'

So Jon had already written her off as Francis Rutland's wife. She could not understand why the thought should distress her so, because she knew only too well what his views were on the subject of their remarriage. It could never take place.

'Yes, it's an idea I could think about, Francis.'

She stared into the fire, oblivious momentarily to everything but the burning pain of loss. Then she pulled herself together and turned to her fiancé with a bright, brittle smile.

'Would you like a drink, Francis? It's a little too early for coffee. I'm afraid we only have a bottle of sherry and even that I share with my brother!'

'Oh, I don't think so, my dear. Do you mind if I get out my pipe?' He felt for pipe and tobacco in his pockets.

'Not at all.'

The noise from upstairs was growing hilarious. So deafening was it that Kathryn and her companion found it necessary to strain their ears to hear one another. Francis settled back on his side of the couch and contentedly smoked his pipe.

'Have you heard anything about the house?' she asked him.

'Oh yes, I meant to tell you. I had a word with the builders, and they will be sending me a specification of the property. Then we can decide what fittings we require, and the type of flooring and central heating we shall want, and so on.' He smiled at her indulgently. 'I won't begrudge you a thing, my dear. I won't even put a ceiling on the amount you will be able to spend. You see how much I trust you.'

Her conscience reared like a frightened horse. If he only knew how little she deserved that trust.

'Would you—would you like to play chess, Francis?'

'That is an excellent idea, Kathryn. At least you would be sitting next to me while we play, wouldn't you?' He smiled at her over the pipe smoke.

Her uneasiness increased. Her fear of being alone with him was approaching a climax. She found the chessmen and the board, drew up a small coffee table and set out the pieces. Kathryn liked the game and became absorbed in it for a while.

'You play well,' Francis said, in between moves. 'You're better at it than my son. He lacks the necessary concentration.'

They finished their game of chess—Francis won—then Kathryn made some coffee. They drank it in companionable silence. Jon's party was now in full swing. There was a shout of laughter from him, followed by Annette's voice and even louder laughter. Someone put on a record, and the music resounded like a great drum through the ceiling.

'I'm really sorry about the noise, Francis. I had no idea there was going to be a party until after I had made my arrangements with you.'

'Never mind, my dear, can't be helped. It is a bit rowdy, I must admit.'

He emptied the contents of his pipe into the fire, which Kathryn had built up high with coal and logs, then he shifted heavily along the couch. 'Kathryn?' His arm went round her and he stroked her hair. He looked into her eyes and Kathryn stiffened. In the lenses of his glasses. she saw the reflection of a pale, frightened girl. She was face to face with herself.

'Kathryn?' he said again, more urgently this time, and moved towards her lips.

She knew that at last she was being forced to come to terms with reality.

The fire in the grate, which had burned so brightly, was dying down, but the room was still warm. Kathryn was alone, except for the dog. She was sitting on the floor, and her back was resting against the armchair. She had changed into slacks and sweater. and she was asleep. The dog was dozing, with his head on her lap.

The party was still going on, but the noise level had been reduced considerably, probably by the appearance of the food. Kathryn was so deeply asleep that she did not wake up even when there was a gentle tap on the door. It opened slowly and the intruder stood and watched the two sleeping figures. He closed the door behind him and walked across to the rug.

Kathryn woke then, bewildered and blinking her eyes, surprised to see him.

Jon stood with his back to the fire, hands behind him. 'Where's Francis?'

'Gone.'

'Gone? What sort of a fiancé is he to go away and leave an attractive siren like you all alone? He can't be normal.'

129

Jon bent down to fondle the dog, who wagged his tail feebly, but didn't move his position.

'Now there's a nice place you're occupying, old lad. Some men would envy you.' He continued to stroke the dog, then looked up suddenly. 'What happened?' he shot at her. 'Did you go frigid on him?'

She bit her lip, recalling the unhappy little scene when she had failed to respond to Francis' restrained lovemaking. He had been patient and kind. 'We'll wait, my dear,' he had said. 'Give it time. So many years of widowhood have taken their toll. I quite understand. I'm a patient man. It will come.'

But Kathryn knew it would not come. It was there, she was sure, because she had not really lost her feelings over the years. She would come alive again, in the arms of the man she loved—if only he loved her.

'What's the matter?' Jon persisted, when he saw the expression on her face. 'Have I inadvertently stumbled on the truth? Well, well, I'll have to give him some lessons, old chap, won't I?'

Kathryn shifted Flop from her lap and got up.

'Would you please take yourself and your dog out of here?'

She brushed her trousers and pushed back her hair.

'Would you believe it, boy, she's literally giving us the brush-off. Shall we cheer her up, Flop—tell her that the unattached males at my party were very disappointed my landlady didn't join us? And that they said she was the best-looking landlady they'd ever seen?'

He saw her lower lip tremble. He went up to her and put his arm across her shoulders. She twisted away violently.

He went back to the dog. 'She's still not forgiven me, Flop, for the way I treated that letter.' He whispered loudly in the dog's ear, 'Shall we use her own words back at her? She's condemned me for a crime I didn't commit.'

She swung round and looked at him questioningly, and he saw the tears on her cheeks. He slipped his finger under the dog's collar and tugged at it gently. 'Come on,' he said. 'We know when we're not wanted.'

He took the dog away with him and the party upstairs went on.

CHAPTER X

KATHRYN slept late next morning, but not as late as the two men. She had a light breakfast and cleared away. There was still no sound from the others. She went upstairs and glanced into Jon's kitchen. She had a shock. Piled as high as stability and gravity would allow were all the unwashed dishes, cutlery and glasses from the party. She knew it would take the men hours to get through it. She also knew what she must do.

She found an apron and tied it over her slacks. She put the crockery into neat piles on the table and when that was full, on the floor under and around the table. She filled the sink with hot foamy suds, and she began her task. She had been going to and fro for some time, washing and drying alternately, before there was any movement in the bedrooms.

She turned at a sound behind her and saw Geoff standing there in his dressing gown. Jon joined him, similarly attired.

'She's doing the washing up, Jon.'

'So she is.'

They stood, half awake, just watching. Then Jon murmured, 'First she does all that typing for me for nothing. Now she's doing the washing-up after a party to which I didn't invite her.' He became wide awake then. 'Does your good nature know no bounds, Miss Swale? What motivates you, I wonder?'

'Put it down to my purely feminine love of order and cleanliness,' she joked.

But Jon had not listened. 'D'you know, Geoff, your sister is too good to be true. I'm sure she has an ulterior motive. What are you after, Miss Swale?'

Geoff snorted. 'Another diamond brooch, I should think.'

'No, not another brooch.' She turned from the sink and grinned at Jon. 'A pair of diamond ear-clips to match it.'

In a swift movement, Jon was behind her. His arm wrapped round her like a vice and he pulled her backwards against his chest.

'You little minx,' he breathed down her neck. 'I shall begin to believe them at the college when they say you're mercenary.'

131

Geoff watched his sister struggle vainly to free herself, and saw Jon laugh and tighten his grip on her still more. Then, with his head on one side, he said,

'D'you know, Jon, I'd have said there was something going on between you two, if I hadn't seen you kissing Annette in a dark corner last night.'

Kathryn went limp and Jon released her at once.

He advanced menacingly on the other man. 'You, Mr. Geoffrey Swale, are telling tales out of school. I shouldn't if I were you. It could do irreparable harm.'

'But I'm only only telling the truth, Jon.'

'Sometimes, dear friend, the truth is not always what it seems.'

Kathryn swung round to face him, her hands dripping water over the floor. 'Now do you see what I mean?' Her voice implored him to understand.

He studied her for a long moment. 'Yes, I see what you mean.' He spoke slowly. 'Message received and understood, Miss Swale.' He paused. 'But there's no need to rub it in, no need at all.'

He handed a tea towel to Geoff, and took one himself.

'And another thing, Geoff—don't keep hearing wedding bells where Kathryn and I are concerned. It's just not on. Your sister and I are agreed about that. Sorry to disappoint you.'

'Is that true, Kath?'

'Yes, Geoff,' his sister answered very quietly.

'But, Kath, it's so ridiculous to keep pretending . . .' Geoffrey persisted.

'Geoff!' She turned on him. 'Will you stop it at once!'

'You heard what your big sister said, Geoffrey. Stop it. At once.'

'Hey, whose side are you on?' Geoff demanded.

'I don't know, boy. My own, I think.' And he ducked as Geoff threatened him with the plate he was drying.

Rehearsals for the play were going well. Sometimes, Max went to Kathryn's house and they rehearsed their parts. He had persuaded her at last to practise the kisses and he taught her how to stage-kiss.

'First, and most important, you must let yourself go. You must make it look like the real thing, although it isn't, you

132

say the word, beautiful.'

Kathryn laughed, and tried to relax in his arms.

'Do you know,' he said, one evening, 'you're the first girl I've come across who hasn't been longing to kiss me. I actually have to persuade you—it makes a pleasant change, sweet!'

Jon seemed to make it his business to be out whenever Max was there. He had only to hear Max's voice in the hall, and he was, it seemed, out of the house before Kathryn had time to close her living-room door.

One Monday morning, Jon called her into his office. His mood was unbearable and he lashed out at her with cutting sarcasm, criticised everything she said and did, then sat down and held his head.

She watched him apprehensively for a few moments. Taking a chance on his anger, she said, 'Late night troubles, Dr. Wright?'

'No,' he barked. 'And even if I had, it's none of your business.'

Still he sat there, his face hidden from her. When at last he removed his hands, she saw that he looked almost haggard.

'Is there anything I can do? I've got some tablets in my desk like aspirin, only better. They might help.'

'Have you? I'm willing to try anything to get rid of this foul headache, not to mention my sore throat.'

She stood up, noticed it was nearly coffee-time and suggested that he took the tablets with him when he went to the dining-room.

His eyes were heavy as he looked at her. 'Could you bring me some coffee, to save me going for it?' He smiled weakly. 'I promise not to insult you this time, as I seem to remember I did once before.'

She was off to the dining-room and back with the hot liquid before he realised she had gone. She shook two tablets out of the bottle on to the teaspoon and handed them to him.

He grumbled about their size, but swallowed them and gulped some coffee.

'If you feel so bad, should you be here?'

'Of course I should be here. I've got a meeting this afternoon.'

'But you're not going to that, surely?'

'Of course I am. Oh, go to your coffee. I want a bit of peace.'

He went to his meeting. He must have gone straight home,

133

because when she arrived there herself, his car was in the side-way, and she heard him moving around in his room.

'Jon?' she called as she walked up the stairs, 'is there any-thing I can do to help?'

She stood on the landing and he came to his bedroom door.

'I'm going to bed.' He closed the door.

'But, Jon, can't I get you some food? Or a hot milk drink?'

He opened the door again. 'Just go away and leave me alone. Don't you know when you're not wanted?'

His choice of words brought a lump to her throat, but she bravely swallowed it and tried again. 'A hot drink would help you to sleep, Jon.'

'Oh, if you insist, I'll have it for the sake of peace and quiet.'

She turned to go downstairs.

'You can use my milk, not yours. And you can go into my kitchen.'

She found a saucepan, heated the milk, and poured it into a mug. Then she ran downstairs for some tablets and raced up again.

'Milk's ready, Jon. May I come in?'

His reply was muffled, so she took a chance and went in.

He was half sitting, half lying in bed, and his face was pale and drawn.

'Headache bad, Jon?'

He didn't answer, just stretched out his hand for the drink, took the proffered tablets and handed the empty cup back to her.

He leaned back and closed his eyes.

'Aren't you going to lie down, Jon?'

He slid down the bed, turned on his side, and she pulled the covers over his shoulders as though he were a child. She stood looking at him for a heartbreaking moment, then went out. She heard what she interpreted as a muffled 'thanks' as she closed his door.

Kathryn was up early next morning. She ran upstairs before leaving for work, to ask Jon if he had any messages for her. She looked for him in every room. His flat was empty. She could hardly believe that he had gone, but apparently he had.

When she arrived at the college, he was at his desk as usual.

'You're late,' he snapped, as she knocked and entered.

'I'm—I'm sorry. I assumed you would be staying at home to-day, so I——'

'So you thought you'd take advantage of it and get in late, I suppose?'

'Of course not.' Her indignation made him look up. 'I missed the bus because I went upstairs to look for you to see if there was anything you wanted. But you had gone.'

He shrugged his shoulders. Then he sneezed. He continued to sneeze at frequent intervals throughout the day.

'Wouldn't you be better at home, Dr. Wright? You'll only prolong your cold if you don't give in to it at this stage.'

'When I want your advice, I'll ask for it. Right now, I want to do some work. *If* you don't mind.'

She drew in her lips so that the tears would not even start to come, and as she worked, became defiant instead of tearful. 'If that's how he's going to receive my offers of help and sympathy,' she thought, 'then he can jump in the lake. For two pins, I'd tell him that.'

He went home ten minutes early, and when Kathryn arrived he was in bed again. But this time, she didn't go near him. She had her tea and went out to a rehearsal.

Afterwards, Max took her for coffee and it was late when he dropped her at the house.

Geoff met her in the hall. The dog was with him on his lead.

'Where've you been all this time? Jon's been asking for you the whole evening, and even I didn't know where you were.'

'I've been at rehearsal, then I had coffee with Max. Why should I worry about Jon? He's insulted me so much the last few days that I decided I would keep out of his way in future. And you can tell him that from me.' She snatched the lead from his hand. 'I'll take Flop for a walk.' She slammed the front door behind her and marched down the steps and along the road.

She knew he would be at his desk next morning. She waited for his summons, but it did not come. Eventually she decided to go in without being asked. As she closed his door behind her, he looked up and said,

'What are you doing in here? I thought you were going to keep out of my way in future?'

She looked blank.

'I heard what you said last night. You woke me up.'

135

'I'm sorry.'

He leaned back in his chair and swivelled from side to side. 'And I'm sorry about the insults, but as I've told you before, that's me. If you can't take them, then you'd better try and find someone else to work for me.'

She walked across the room to her chair, sat down angrily, opened her notebook and gripped her pencil so hard her knuckles whitened.

He watched her and waited. 'When you are in a calmer frame of mind, I'll begin.'

All the names which Max had called him in the past crowded into her mind. She began to understand how Max felt about him.

His voice broke into her rebellious thoughts. He said softly, 'Am I making you hate me?'

Tears reached danger level. She stared at him, her eyes wide, her face ashen. 'But why, Jon, why?'

He did not answer, just played with his pen.

She controlled her tears. 'Oh, forget it. Let's get on.'

Slowly the year was moving towards the spring. The weather was improving and the sun was beginning to warm the earth. Kathryn was conscious of a new feeling in the air as she went down the steps on Saturday morning to go shopping. She was walking past Jon's car, parked as usual in the side-way, when she heard a voice call her name from an upstairs window.

She turned and saw Jon.

'Going shopping? Wait a moment, and I'll take you.'

Her first impulse was to ignore him, but she relented. Knowing he was just getting over his cold, she did not want to bring him down the stairs for nothing, so she stood at the side of his car and waited. He came out of the house, his dog at his heels, and let Kathryn into the passenger seat. He opened the rear door for Flop, who bounded into the back, then snuffled affectionately at Kathryn's neck. She laughed and pushed him away.

Jon reprimanded the dog and gave him a sharp order to 'sit', then he turned the car out of the drive and into the road.

'I was going out, anyway, so I thought I might as well drop you at the shops.'

'Are you feeling better?' She made her voice impersonal.

136

'Thank you, yes.' He grinned at her. 'Hope I haven't given it to you.'

'I doubt it. I never seem to catch other people's colds.'

'Famous last words! I only hope you're right, for my sake. Can't have my secretary away ill. I've got too much work on hand at present.'

'Thank you for those kind unselfish thoughts.' Kathryn said sarcastically.

He merely grinned again and drew up at the kerb. 'Get out quick. There's a double yellow line here. I don't want to be caught by a traffic warden.'

She got out on the pavement, and spotted Max. Holding the car door open, she called to him across the heads of the Saturday morning shoppers and he turned immediately.

'Why, hallo, beautiful.' He stretched his hand towards her.

'Wait for me, Max. I'm going to the supermarket, too. You can carry my shopping bag for me.'

'Of course, then we can have a coffee.'

'I take it you'll want your handbag?' The curt voice from the car made her turn back to Jon. She bent down, took her bag and said, 'Yes, please. Thanks for the lift.'

He leaned across and slammed her door shut. 'Don't mention it.'

Max gave Kathryn a meaningful look, and Jon watched them walk across the pavement to the shop. Max took Kathryn's shopping bag, then entwined his fingers with hers.

The driver savagely started the engine and it stalled. He cursed and pressed the starter again. It fired into life, then he momentarily forgot his road drill. He pulled out without looking back over his right shoulder and narrowly missed becoming involved with a cyclist who had started to overtake him. He swore at himself and drove on.

Kathryn enjoyed wandering round the large self-service store with Max. They were walking to the check-out when a husky feminine voice called out,

'Why, Miss Swale, what a coincidence, seeing you in here.'

Kathryn knew who it was without turning round. She also knew she would have been ignored if it hadn't been for her handsome escort.

'Oh, good morning, Miss Linton. I don't think you two have

137

met before. Miss Linton, this is Max Rutland, the principal's son. Max—Annette Linton, head of the domestic science department at the college.'

Annette's eyes went to work at once. They began their exploratory journey over Max's face, and Max responded in good measure. He liked what he saw, there was no doubt about that.

'I had no idea Mr. Rutland had a son, let alone a completely adult son.' She gave the word 'adult' the full treatment.

Max still said nothing, just looked.

To fill the awkward pause while they silently conversed, Kathryn said, 'Max is taking part in the students' play next Wednesday, aren't you, Max?'

'Yes, oh—er—yes. You should come and see it, Miss Linton.'

'Oh, Annette, Max, please.' Kathryn noted the subtle invitation in the words. So did Max. He looked at his watch.

'We two are going to have a coffee. If you've finished your shopping, will you join us, Annette?'

'Do you know, I'm dying for a coffee, Max. If you two will just wait for me outside, I'll show you a good little place where they do the most delicious brew imaginable.'

So Kathryn and Max paid for their goods and waited obediently for Annette to join them.

'I'm warning you, Max . . .'

He held up his hand. 'No need, sweet. Most men know what they're about when they meet a woman like that.'

She looked at him in astonishment. 'That was more or less what Jon said.' At the question in his eyes, she said, 'She's Jon's girl-friend at the moment.'

'She is? You'd hardly guess, would you?' His voice was dry.

'Here she comes. A final word of warning, Max . . .'

'Don't worry, sweet.' His voice held urgent reassurance.

Annette was right about the coffee. It was delicious. Kathryn's two companions were carrying on both an audible and a silent conversation which was quite outside her sphere. She was seeing a side of Max which was new, and which she did not like very much. Annette had that effect on men, she noticed. Even Jon changed when he was in her company.

At last they remembered her. 'I'm so sorry, Miss Swale, if we have left you out in the cold. You must have been bored stiff. But it's not often one meets such an interesting man.' She turned her deep brown eyes to Max. 'I'm giving a party next

138

Saturday, Max, and Miss Swale, of course. I should be delighted if you would both come. Would you?' The urgency in her eyes had the desired effect on the man she was addressing.

'I believe I had an engagement, but I can easily break it.' He smiled. 'I'll be delighted to accept your invitation. And you, sweet?' to Kathryn. 'Coming to the party?'

Annette's eyes narrowed suspiciously at the apparent familiarity between them.

'I'd love to, thanks. It will be something to look forward to after the excitement of the play. Are you coming to see it on Wednesday, Miss Linton? Max is the leading man.'

'Oh,' her voice was heavy with meaning, 'then I shall definitely not miss it.' She rose, gathered her handbag and gloves. 'Next Saturday, then? Eightish? Goodbye, Max.'

When she had gone, Max lifted up his hand. 'Say nothing, beautiful, nothing at all. Now I'll take you home.'

'Geoff,' Kathryn called as she let herself in to the house. 'Geoff, where are you?'

Kathryn sprinted up the stairs and went into his living-room. Then she stopped. He was playing chess with Jon.

'Oh, I thought you were alone.'

Jon half rose, and said with a mocking smile, 'I'll leave if you want to go all confidential.'

'No, don't go.'

Jon noted her sparkling eyes and broad smile. 'Sure it was plain coffee you had and that it wasn't laced with brandy?' He looked at her harder and continued. 'There's a sort of gloating air about you, Miss Swale, that makes me feel vaguely suspicious. Come on, give.'

'Geoff,' she ignored Jon's remark, 'guess who I had coffee with.'

'Don't tell me—Max.'

'Who else?'

'The Old Boy?'

Kathryn shook her head and looked triumphantly at Jon. 'Annette.'

Jon's head shot round. 'How did that come about? I wouldn't have said you were on coffee terms with her. She's hardly your type.'

'No.' Still the smile clung to her mouth. 'But she's Max's

type. And he's hers.' She turned to go out. 'Carry on with your chess.' She waved her hand.

'Come back here, Miss Swale. What was that penultimate remark supposed to mean? Apart from being a good exit line.'

'Oh, we met in the supermarket, and she turned on the charm, as she usually does when there's an unattached male around,' she gazed boldly into Jon's narrowed eyes, 'and like all the rest, Max fell for it. He invited her to coffee with us, and being Annette, she accepted. From then on, I took a back seat. I didn't mind, of course, because I could sit back and watch her at work, luring her next victim into her spider's web.'

Jon leaned back and crossed his legs. 'No doubt you picked up a few tips.'

'I wouldn't dirty my hands with her methods.'

'Kath, be careful what you're saying,' Geoff warned.

Jon waved his hand at him. 'It's all right. I'm proof against your sister's bluntness.'

'She's invited us to her party.' The smile reappeared.

'What party?'

Kathryn was enjoying herself. 'The party she's giving next Saturday. Hasn't she told you about it?'

'She certainly hasn't.'

'Perhaps she doesn't intend to invite you. You know, off with the old love, on with the new.'

This shot scored a bull's-eye. Jon got up and walked towards her retreating figure, dusting his hands as he went. 'One day in the very near future, *Mrs. Wright*, you will get that good hiding you so consistently ask for. In the meantime, take your brother's advice and be careful what you are saying.'

She dived down the stairs out of reach, the smile still on her face.

She awoke next morning with a sore throat, a headache and no smile. She felt terrible. She went up to Geoff's room.

'He's given it to me. Geoff. I knew he would. He didn't go home when I told him to. Now what am I going to do?'

'Given you what?' Jon stood at the landing outside Geoff's door. She turned to him, a hand at her throat.

'You've caught my cold?' He threw back his head and laughed loudly. He mimicked her voice, ' "I never catch other people's

140

colds". I hate to say "I told you so", but, as I said, famous last words.'

His lack of sympathy, on top of her affliction, made her furious. 'Serves you right if I'm off work.'

He could have been annoyed at her tone, but he wasn't. He was irritatingly mild. 'If I kept on working, why can't you?'

She made an exasperated sound and went downstairs.

'She's worried about the play on Wednesday, Jon,' she heard Geoff say as she retreated.

'Is that all?' Jon dismissed the subject. 'She's got an understudy, hasn't she?'

As the day progressed, her sore throat worsened, and she had an early night.

She got up on Monday morning, feeling sluggish and depressed.

There was a tap on her door, and Jon called out, 'In view of your condition, can I give you a lift?'

'No, *thank* you,' Kathryn answered, without opening the door.

'If that's how you feel about it, you can do the other thing!' he shouted back, and slammed out of the house. As soon as he had gone, Kathryn regretted her childish action. It would have been so comfortable and warm in the car.

Jon did not give her an ounce of sympathy all day. He expected her to keep up her usual standard of efficiency, and when occasionally her attention wandered, he called her back without mercy.

She missed the rehearsal that evening. She told the producer that she had a slight cold, and thought it wiser to nurse it at home.

'Don't forget the dress rehearsal tomorrow evening, Miss Swale,' he reminded her. 'Hope you can make it. We'll have to get your understudy up to scratch, just in case.'

'Oh, it will be better by then,' she assured him.

But it got worse instead of better. She began to sneeze, and drooped so noticeably that even Geoff was concerned. He urged her to go to bed, which she did, and offered to make her a milk drink, which she gladly accepted. While she was waiting for him to bring it in, she got out of bed to find her tablets, extracted two from the bottle.

'Here's your milk, Kathy.'

141

She swung round to see Jon standing in the centre of the room. She scurried back to bed and pulled up the covers, her face flushed, her hair dishevelled.

He looked down at her. 'You resemble a timid little girl.' He lowered the milk carefully on to the bedside table, and put his hand on her forehead. 'You're a bit hot. Your temperature's probably up a bit, but that's only to be expected. If you feel like I felt, then you must feel bad.' His expression was almost kind, and it melted Kathryn's heart.

'Thank you for bringing my milk, Jon. I did ask Geoff.'

'Just thought I'd return the compliment you paid me. Drink up, there's a good girl.' She drank up, obediently, while he wandered round the room, picking up ornaments and pictures, and inspecting them closely.

'It's obvious from all your feminine knick-knacks and precious possessions that you live like a bachelor girl. Life is strange, isn't it?' He stood at the side of the bed and looked down at her, lost in thought. His shoulders lifted and fell in a kind of hopeless gesture.

She lay back on the pillow and closed her eyes, and he bent down and pulled the covers over her as she had done to him. She looked at him and smiled, and his smile in return was the sweetest she had ever seen.

CHAPTER XI

'WHY are you in this morning, Miss Swale?' Jon's terse voice made her jump, and she snapped shut her powder compact and slipped it guiltily into her handbag. She raked his face for a sign of the tenderness he had shown her the evening before, but none was there, and her glance ricocheted off the hard line of his jaw.

'Well? I'm waiting?'

She licked dry lips which were cracking from her cold and sat down. Her legs felt oddly weak. She still had not fully recovered her breath from the strangely difficult feat of walking up the stairs.

'To work, I suppose. What else?'

'In my humble opinion, you're not in a fit state to work.'

'As you said yourself, if you could do it, so can I.'

He regarded her intently for a moment. 'Ah, now I get it. Tonight, no doubt, is the dress rehearsal. You could hardly go to that, I suppose, and not come in to work.'

'I don't want to let them down.'

'Don't you? Or is it the thought of your understudy kissing your boy-friend on the stage, instead of yourself?'

She shook her head forlornly. 'If you want to think that, how can I stop you? If I told you I came in because I remembered the conference you—we—are attending next week, and realised we should have to keep up with the work, you wouldn't believe me.'

He was silent for a moment. 'You are not indispensable, as I've said before. There are others who could do your work.'

She turned weary eyes up to his. 'Can we stop arguing and get on?'

So they worked. At coffee-time, Jon told her he would walk with her to the dining-room. He had to slow his pace to hers.

'I'm sorry, Jon, I just can't walk fast today.'

'You little idiot,' he hissed, 'why did you come in? I've a good mind to carry you out to my car and take you home forcibly.'

Kathryn looked around furtively at the students milling about in the corridors and hoped they had not heard him.

Jon held the dining-room door open for her. 'If you haven't improved by lunch-time, you're going home, whether you want to or not.'

They parted to go to separate tables.

Kathryn joined Jill and her other friends. 'You look washed out, Kath. You should be at home.'

'Don't you start, Jill. I've just had a lecture from Dr. Wright.'

'What? Has he suddenly become considerate? Must be something wrong with him.'

'The dress rehearsal's tonight. I've got to keep going for that.'

'Jon darling, so you've honoured us with your presence this morning.' They all turned at the sound of Annette's voice, as she took her place beside him.

Kathryn's friends squirmed, 'Ugh! How he can stand her

beats me,' whispered Jill. 'They're obviously as thick as thieves. She's got him where she wants him, hasn't she?'

'Jon,' Annette was saying, 'do you know about my party? Did Miss Swale tell you?'

Jon's eyes darted across to Kathryn and he smiled reminiscently. 'Yes, she told me.'

'You will come, Jon? I knew I need not ask you specially because you're always at my place, darling, aren't you? You're almost part of the furniture.'

Jon pretended to be annoyed. 'If that's how you look on me . . .'

'Oh, but darling, of course it isn't.' She seized one of his hands and put it to her lips.

Jim Mexby sat down at their table and said caustically, 'Keep that for later, Annette, can't you?'

She turned large, innocent eyes to the speaker. 'I don't know what you mean, Mr. Mexby.' She lowered their linked hands to the table top, and Jon made no attempt to take his away.

'No?' Jim Mexby's smile was sardonic.

Suddenly Jon stubbed out his cigarette, rose, and looked at Kathryn. 'Coming, Miss Swale?'

Taken completely off guard, Kathryn coloured deeply and swallowed the remains of her coffee. As they walked together to the door, she knew that Annette's eyes were following them. She knew also that Annette would not take Jon's snub lightly. But what could Annette do that would harm her in Jon's eyes? His opinion of her had already hit rock-bottom.

Kathryn looked questioningly at Jon as he held the door open for her, but he offered no explanation of his abrupt departure with her at his side.

'Come in when you're ready, will you?' was all he said, as they arrived at their respective rooms.

'While I remember,' Kathryn said, as she took her seat opposite him, 'Francis has asked me to confirm that you have our tickets for the conference next week. And should he have them?'

Jon searched inside a drawer. 'Yes, here they are.' He tossed them across his desk. 'He'd better have them. Once I get there, you won't see much of me. I'll be too busy.'

'And the name of the hotel?'

'The Turrets,' he told her, and she wrote it down. 'The whole

144

party is booked in there. It was much easier to do it that way.'

Later she called to see Francis. He came across as she stood at his door. 'My dear, you look quite ill. Should you be here?'

'I must keep going, Francis. The play's tomorrow evening.'

'That's all very well, Kathryn, but if you're not fit enough ... I suggest, my dear, that you come home with me this evening and have a hot meal. Max will be there, and you could have a word with him about the play.'

The thought of a proper meal with someone else doing the cooking was certainly tempting to Kathryn, and she accepted with pleasure.

'You'll have to go home early,' Jon told her, as he signed some letters. 'You look half dead.'

'I can't. I'm going to Francis' for a meal. Then I'm going to the rehearsal. With Max.'

Jon appeared to go dumb. He extracted a cigarette from the packet and motioned her out of the room. She went.

Francis called for her at five o'clock. She looked at herself in the cloakroom mirror and was horrified. Surely she didn't really look as ill as that?

'My dear,' Francis said, as he drove her to his home, 'you need cosseting. How can you possibly go to this rehearsal? From the look of you, you won't be fit enough for the performance tomorrow night, let alone this evening. Haven't you an understudy?'

'Yes, of course, but it would hardly be fair to Max or the others if I couldn't make it.'

'Your sense of duty is too strong. We are all dispensable, even if we like to think we're not.'

The idea of a cooked meal proved to be more attractive in theory than in practice. Kathryn did her best with the plateful of food which Francis' housekeeper had put in front of her, but her appetite did not please her fiancé.

'You've scarcely touched it, my dear.'

Max was very concerned. 'Look, sweet, you can't possibly make it tonight. And I honestly doubt whether you'll make it tomorrow for the actual performance. Come on, Kathryn, give in. There's always Maureen, your understudy. She's good, you know, even in the kissing bits. I told you, most girls like kissing me!'

145

She smiled weakly and realised that he was right. Almost in tears, she took her leave of Francis, and got into Max's car. He was taking her home on his way to the rehearsal.

'Don't come in tomorrow, whatever happens, Kathryn,' her fiancé told her. 'Have the day off. I absolutely insist.'

Max helped her up the steps in to the house. As they stood outside her bedroom door, he put his arms round her waist.

'I'm so sorry to let you down, Max.' Her eyes grew moist.

'It's a real shame, sweet, after all your hard work. I've enjoyed working with you. I must tell you that.'

The front door opened and closed, but he ignored the fact. He raised his hand and stroked her hair.

'Don't come too near me, Max. You might catch it.'

'It would be heaven to catch something from you, sweet,' he whispered as footsteps went up the staircase, followed by four furry, golden paws.

'So here goes.' He kissed her gently on the lips. 'Goodnight, sleep well. And do what Father says—stay at home tomorrow.'

'Good luck with the play, Max.'

'Thanks, sweet. See you some time.' He raised his hand and was gone.

Kathryn slept most of next day. Early that morning she had struggled out of bed and asked Geoff to tell Jon she would be away from work. He had passed her message on to Jon before he left the house, but Jon had apparently said he was already aware of it.

When she awoke the following morning, she felt much better. Her cold seemed to have improved, and her legs were once again willing to support her. She called upstairs to her brother that she was going back to work, and when she walked into her office, Jill was surprised to see her.

'Kath! Why on earth have you come in? I was coping, dear. You must have tamed your boss, he's been so much easier to work for this time. What have you done to him? Or is it Annette's influence?'

'I wouldn't know. But I'm almost back to normal today, Jill, so I thought I'd come back. Better than sitting around at home. Where is Dr. Wright, by the way?'

'In London, at a meeting. He won't be back today. He did say that if you were silly enough to come in—his words—then you could just sit around and look pretty. He also said you could go in his room and do anything you liked except put your feet up on his desk!'

That sounded so like Jon that they laughed. Kathryn decided then to overhaul the filing system and trace one or two lost letters. During the afternoon, she called to see Francis. He said he was delighted to see her looking better.

'Did you go to the play, Francis? Was it good, and did Max do well? How did my understudy get on? I haven't had a chance to ask anyone about it yet.'

'Sit down, my dear, and I'll try to answer all your questions. Yes, the play was good and Max was excellent. Your understudy managed very well, too. I think Max helped her along. Although he's my son, I must admit he is a very good actor.'

Max had sent a message telling her he would collect her on Saturday evening and take her to the party.

'Do you mind if I go, Francis? Miss Linton was kind enough to invite me as well as Max, so I didn't like to refuse.'

'Go, my dear, by all means. Enjoy yourselves. It's not my cup of tea at all.'

Francis took her home, but he would not go in. He waved and drove away.

Jon's voice was brisk and businesslike next day. 'Come in, Miss Swale.' His face was impassive when his glance flicked over her. He helped himself to a cigarette and held his lighter to it.

'I take it you're better.'

'Yes, thank you.'

'If a little subdued.'

'As you say, subdued.'

His eyes assessed her as he waved away the smoke and leaned back. 'No doubt as a result of missing the play.'

'No doubt.'

He placed his smouldering cigarette on the ashtray and pulled the pile of papers towards him.

'Well, after that scintillating piece of conversation, we will proceed with our work.'

He started reading a letter at the top of the pile, then, as if his mind was not really on it, asked her how she had occupied herself the previous day.

147

'I reorganised the filing system, and brought it bang up to date. It's something I've been wanting to do for years.'

He nodded briefly and continued with his reading.

A few seconds later, he said with a smile, 'In that case I'd better go out for the day more often. Then you might get the department so well organized there would be no need for a head of it.'

'You mean I could make you redundant?' Her smile challenged him. 'It's certainly an idea worth working on. Thanks for the tip.'

He looked amused. 'You're regaining your form. You must be feeling better.'

After that, he gave his whole attention to his work.

Kathryn felt curiously elated about going to the party. She put on the only party dress she possessed—it was white silky satin, with a halter neck, low-cut at the back, revealing her smooth white shoulders and allowing her hair to swing free and shining round her neck.

She pinned on her diamond brooch and as she admired its incredible sparkle, felt just a little defiant. Why should she not wear it? She need not tell anyone who gave it to her. Just a friend of the family, she would say—a very old friend. A very good friend.

It caught Max's eye as soon as Kathryn opened the door.

'What's this? Got a rich uncle? He's spoilt you, whoever he is. That brooch is fabulous.'

'Yes, a rich uncle, that's right.'

He looked at her curiously, but merely said, 'Where's your coat?'

She put a lacy white stole round her shoulders and slipped into her coat which Max held open for her.

'Annette gave me a special reminder to bring you, Max. Aren't you flattered?'

He smiled. 'Of course I'm flattered. My masculine ego takes a bow. But I'd be a darned sight more flattered if it had been you who'd said it.'

Helen chased along the drive towards them. 'Can you wait for us, Max? I'm late as usual.'

Max answered, 'Be delighted to give you a lift, Helen.'

'I'll tell Geoff. Hope he's ready.'

Geoff was ready. 'This is nice of you, Max. Now we can arrive in style.'

It was not far to Annette's flat. She greeted them on the doorstep, looking wonderful in a red velvet dress which clung to her figure. Her lacquered black hair was secured at the back by a filmy red scarf. Long golden, pendant earrings emphasised her small ears, and gold bangles decorated her wrists.

Her eyes saw only Max, and she linked her arm in his, calling over her shoulder to the two women to help themselves to combs and powder.

They tidied themselves at the triple-mirrored dressing-table and Helen soon joined Geoff in the lounge, leaving Kathryn standing alone in the doorway She searched the room for Jon and saw him leaning against the wall near the fireplace. His eyes strayed over her as she moved into the centre of the room, lowering her eyelids against the pall of cigarette smoke which already hung like a moorland mist over the heads of the guests.

Jon watched her standing there, looking shy and uncertain.

He watched, but he made no move to go to her At last, she found some courage and walked across to Max. At that moment in time, he was a safe harbour and she was thankful as his hand came out towards her as if he sensed her shyness.

Still Jon stood there, lazily smoking, watching and narrowing his eyes as he saw Max draw Kathryn to his side and include her in the conversation. Kathryn listened to the talk around her, and found her eyes straying, against her will, to the isolated observant figure of her former husband. She flushed as she met his cynical expression and turned her head away from him to give her full attention to those nearby.

Max asked her, 'What are you having, sweet? Sherry?'

'Please, Max.'

As he handed Kathryn her drink, Annette spoke to him. 'So glad you made it, Max. My party wouldn't have been the same without you.'

He answered the caress in her eyes with a mocking bow.

'My word, Miss Swale,' Annette was gazing intently at Kathryn's dress, 'what a beautiful brooch, if I may say so. Did you, I wonder, beg, borrow, steal it, or—acquire it by other means?'

'I—I . . .' Kathryn floundered, thrown off balance by the manner in which Annette had focussed attention on her.

149

'She says a rich uncle gave it to her,' Max told the others, who were all staring at the object under discussion. Everyone laughed.

'That's her story, and she's sticking to it.' They all turned at the sound of Jon's voice. 'But judging by her confusion, I should say she got it "by other means".'

Kathryn almost foundered at his treachery. She saw the sardonic amusement on his face and knew she would get no help from him. So she said, with a careless laugh,

'Well, you wouldn't expect me to tell you the truth, now would you?'

Max frowned. 'Don't speak like that, sweet, or I shall have to change my high opinion of you. Don't disillusion me.'

'Oh, Max!' Annette laughed up at him. 'Are you trying to tell us that you still have illusions about us women? We're all the same at heart, you know—out for what we can get.'

Kathryn wanted desperately to say 'speak for yourself'. She watched Geoff move to the centre of the group. His hostess had plainly provoked him beyond endurance. 'Annette should learn not to go from the particular to the general. She can speak for herself, not for my sister, and certainly not for my girl-friend.' To soften his words a little to suit the mood of the gathering, he put his arm round Helen's shoulders and pulled her close. 'I've got no money, and my girl-friend knows she can't get anything out of me. But she still loves me, and so far I haven't noticed her eyes straying to other men who have more to offer.'

' "So far" are the operative words, brother.' Everyone laughed as Jon spoke and Kathryn saw that his eyes were fixed on her.

Max intercepted the look and frowned from one to the other. His arm moved protectively round Kathryn's shoulders. Annette saw the action. 'Max, come over here. I want you to meet some friends of mine.'

Max whispered in Kathryn's ear, 'Won't be long,' and followed Annette across the room.

Kathryn finished her drink and amused herself by studying the other guests. She knew Jon was still watching her and she wanted to throw off his eyes, but they clung like iron filings to a magnet no matter what she did.

He startled her when he appeared at her side. He murmured, 'Can your rich uncle get you another drink?'

150

She had to smile, and handed him her empty glass. He was soon back. 'There you are, niece.'

'Thank you, Uncle Jon.' She smiled up at him demurely and he took Max's place on the arm of her chair. His hand moved behind her and his fingers trailed the bare flesh of her shoulder.

He leaned down and whispered, 'Has anyone told you how beautiful you look?'

'No.'

'Well, I'm telling you now. I'm glad I've got such a charming niece.'

She looked up at him. 'My uncle is pretty good, too.'

Their eyes came together and clung, and for a few seconds everyone else in the room faded away, and they were two people alone in a wilderness. The world rocked around her, and she dragged her eyes from his and tried to pull herself back to reality.

'Kathryn, sweet, come over here.' Max approached and drew her out of the armchair. 'I want you to convince these people that I'm not your fiancé, but your future stepson. They won't believe me.'

She looked apologetically at Jon, who frowned as Max pulled her into the circle of laughing people. 'Now tell them, Kathryn. You're going to marry my father. Go on, say it.'

'It's quite true. I'm his father's future wife.' She turned to Max. 'He's going to be my stepson, my little boy. Aren't you, dear?'

'Yes, Mummy.' Max's high-pitched small-child voice had them roaring with laughter, especially when he crouched down, seized Kathryn's hand and looked up at her. 'Sweetie, Mummy?' he asked plaintively.

'You'd better cut that out, Max,' said one of the men, 'or we might misunderstand your meaning.'

They all laughed again and Max resumed his normal height. 'That's all right by me. What about you?' His arm encircled her waist. Kathryn shook her head and laughed helplessly.

'Well,' Max addressed the others, 'now do you believe me?'

'Not when you're cuddling her like that.'

Kathryn smiled. 'I don't mind. I look upon him as a brother. A nice brother.'

Max's hand flew to his head. 'Oh no. I am prostrate with despair. Anything but a brother.'

'That puts you in your place, Max.' Annette was at his side. 'Try me. I wouldn't look upon you as a brother.' Her brown eyes searched his.

'I'm darned sure you wouldn't.' Geoff was standing behind Kathryn, and his words came from under his breath.

Max looked her coolly up and down. 'Do I take that as an invitation, Annette?'

'Take it how you like, Max.'

Jon touched her on the shoulder. 'Isn't it time we had some food?'

'Food, darling?' She hung on to his arm. 'But of course. Help me distribute it, darling, will you? After all you know the geography of my kitchen better than anyone else here.'

'Only of your kitchen?' Geoff murmured.

'Geoff, be quiet. Someone might hear you.' His sister frowned. 'Helen, keep him in order, dear.'

'You heard what Kath said, Geoff darling. After all, you are accepting Annette's hospitality, aren't you?'

'Oh, all right.' He was like a sulky boy. 'But you can't stop me thinking it.'

Helen kissed him quickly on the cheek.

The buffet supper, when it appeared, tantalised the eyes as well as the appetite. It was as good to look at as the hostess herself who, with the help of some of her guests, set it out on the extended dining table which had been pushed to one side of the room.

Kathryn sat beside Max on the couch while they ate the colourful and enticing savouries which Annette had so expertly created. The tiny cakes and the iced gâteaux, overflowing on to the plates with whipped cream, were a challenge to the palate.

'No wonder Jon comes here for his meals,' Kathryn thought as she drank her second cup of Annette's delicious coffee.

Max was as appreciative as everyone else.

'She's not head of the domestic science deparment for nothing, is she?' Helen reminded them. 'She's got a string of diplomas and qualifications as long as a clothes line.'

'Someone's missing a good wife,' one of the men commented. 'If I weren't married, Annette, I'd ask you to marry me. You're a darn good cook.'

'Is that all you'd marry me for, Mike? My cooking?' She looked insinuatingly at him.

'Well,' he looked at her consideringly, 'I'll tell you the answer to that one in private.'

Everyone laughed. Annette began to talk about Max's part in the students' play. Kathryn looked round for Jon. He was nowhere in sight, and although she was surrounded by people, she felt oddly lonely.

Then Annette disappeared. Kathryn found it impossible to tether her attention to the conversation around her. Where had they gone? What were they doing?

'Now look what I've done!' Max's annoyance broke into the anguish of her thoughts. 'Spilt coffee down my jacket.'

'Annette's got something to clean that up with,' one of the wives told him. 'You'll have to look for her. She's not around in here.'

Max took Kathryn's hand and pulled her up. 'Come on, Stepmum. Come and clean up your little boy.' Laughter followed them out of the room.

As they turned into the hall, Jon was lifting his lips from Annette's inviting mouth.

'Sorry to interrupt, Annette.' Max gave her an odd look. 'But we've been told you have something to remove a coffee stain.' He indicated the damp brown mark down his jacket.

'Yes, of course, Max. It's on the dressing-table in my bedroom. The bottle's marked cleaning fluid. I was using it myself this evening. Shall I do it for you?'

'No, no, stay where you are. I wouldn't dream of being a spoilsport.' He gave Jon a calculated glance. 'I'll take my girl instead. She'll do it. She does anything I want, don't you, beautiful?'

'Now, now, Max.' Annette drawled her words. 'If that's what you have in mind, you'd better lock the door. It's all right with me. I'm sure Kathryn wouldn't welcome any interruptions.'

'You hear what she says, sweet.' Max's voice was indolent and suggestive. 'We'd better take her advice and lock the door.' He smiled at the harshness in the other man's eyes. 'Come on, beautiful, lead me to it. I can't wait.' He dropped a light kiss on Kathryn's cheek.

As Max led Kathryn towards the bedroom door, Annette's arms crept round Jon's neck. She turned her face upwards and puckered her lips for another kiss. But Jon pulled her hands away, turned sharply and went into the lounge, leaving her standing by herself in the hall looking stupefied and angry.

Max closed the bedroom door. 'What goes on between those two? Who's chasing who, I wonder?' He shrugged and walked to the dressing-table. 'Here's the stuff.' He removed his jacket and held it out to her. 'Clean it up for me, like a good stepmum.'

Kathryn applied the fluid with her handkerchief and eventually the stain disappeared. Max watched her as she worked.

'Did I tell you, by the way, that my father isn't too well?'

'No, Max.' Kathryn was shocked. 'What's wrong? He hasn't—he surely hasn't caught my cold?'

'Sorry to say, sweet, he's got a sore throat and headache, all the usual symptoms. Said he was going to bed early.'

'Oh, Max, why didn't you tell me earlier? I wouldn't have come to the party. I would have gone to him instead.'

'That, beautiful, is exactly why I didn't tell you. He wanted me not to.'

'But I'll come tomorrow, Max. I must look after him. It was my fault—I shouldn't have gone near him when I had it. Thank goodness you didn't catch it.'

'No.' He touched her lips with his fingers. 'And I asked for it, didn't I? I kissed you, remember?' He seemed to grow restless. 'Have you finished yet? That'll do. I'll send it to the cleaners.' He put the jacket on. 'Thanks, sweet. You're a good girl. Now I'm going.' He edged to the door, keen to get away. 'Coming?'

'When I've combed my hair.'

Max took his handkerchief and dabbed at the wet mark on his jacket. 'Shows a bit.'

He opened the door. Jon was outside, his hand extended towards the handle. Max narrowed his eyes, turned back to Kathryn, raised the handkerchief to his mouth. 'Is it all off, sweet?' He rubbed his lips.

'Is what all off?' She turned from the mirror and saw Jon.

'Why, your lipstick, of course.'

'But, Max, what are you——'

Max looked in the mirror. 'Ah yes, it's all gone. 'Bye, sweetheart.' His voice was intimate. 'Come back to me soon, won't you?'

He smiled broadly as he passed Jon, and indicated the room with a wave of his hand. 'Your turn now?'

It was obvious that Jon only just prevented himself from

154

swinging his fist at him. The door closed, the key rasped as it was turned in the lock.

'It's not true, what you're thinking, Jon. It's simply not true. You must believe me. I've been cleaning his jacket.'

It was as if he had not heard. His eyes, contemptuous and ice cold, tore her self-respect to shreds. His voice, when he spoke, held a grating quality she had never heard before.

'Your moral standards have scarcely improved over the years. If anything, they've gone into even greater decline.'

'But, Jon,' Kathryn entreated, 'you surely didn't take seriously what Annette said in the hall. For my sake, please don't believe all the poisonous innuendoes that she chooses to pass off as the truth. Geoff warned you what she was like. Her insinuations are calculated and deadly. I beg you not to let her taint your judgment.'

His voice was dangerously quiet. 'Are you asking me even now not to believe what my eyes tell me?'

'But, Jon, your eyes have told you nothing. It's your mind yet again that's following false evidence and misinterpreting the facts.'

Her voice rose in desperation as she sensed her inability to get through to him and clear herself in his eyes. 'You said yourself that the truth is not always what it seems.'

As she watched his steps bringing him slowly and relentlessly closer, she knew she had failed to reach him. 'Don't give me that again,' he spat out. 'I've grown resistant to that sort of talk.'

She began to be afraid. He stood in front of her now, his anger at white heat. 'When others have no scruples where you as an engaged woman are concerned, and take with alacrity what is plainly theirs for the asking, why should I, who perhaps have greater claim on you than anyone else, deny myself the pleasure of your considerable charms?' His arms compelled her towards him as she was helpless in his grip if iron. 'If it's warmth and passion you crave, there's no need to turn to your future stepson. I'm more than willing to oblige. I possess a surfeit of such commodities to lavish on women like you.'

He jerked her against him and his mouth came down savage and merciless. He pressed her backwards and down on to the bed, and a sensation of intense joy took possession of her whole being. Now she knew she was back at last where she truly belonged—in the arms of the man she loved. She was engulfed by a desire to submit unreservedly to his demands and she clung to him for endless minutes, yielding to the mastery of his lips and the caressing of his hands with an eager passion which equalled his own. Then it came to her that something was wrong, and that she had no right to be where she was, that she was betrothed to another, and that she was being used by this man as he had apparently used so many other women in the past, merely to indulge the whim of the moment.

She struggled desperately and managed somehow to wrench herself free of his body and stand up.

'My word,' he said, breathing heavily and rising from the bed, 'if you respond to them all like that, no wonder they come back for more.'

Her hand swung upwards, but before it made contact with his cheek, he deftly caught her wrist and gripped it viciously. Tears swamped her eyes and she was choked with anger.

'Who exactly do you think I am? Annette? Or one of your girl-friends whom you can pick up and throw down as the fancy takes you?'

She twisted her wrist from his grasp. The loud-voiced chatter, the roars of laughter, the beat of the music became raucous and mocking in the background. She looked wildly into his eyes, seeking compassion but meeting only derision and contempt.

'Kathryn?' Max's voice splintered the brittle silence between them. 'Kathryn sweet, where are you?'

Jon smiled sarcastically. 'Your boy-friend is calling. Won't you tell him where you are?'

Kathryn did not stir.

'Then if you won't, I will.'

'No, don't, Jon. Please.' She laid a restraining hand on his arm, but he threw it off, walked to the door, opened it and called, 'Kathryn's in here. With me.'

Max appeared in the doorway, looked from one to the other, saw the sardonic smile on Jon's face and Kathryn's dishevelled appearance. 'Oh,' he said, heavily, 'sorry if I interrupted something,' and turned and walked slowly away.

'Tit for tat,' Jon remarked with much satisfaction. He gave her an exaggeratedly low bow. 'Goodnight, Miss Swale. And—thank you.'

He went out and closed the door behind him.

CHAPTER XII

SHE was in the little sports car, speeding through the darkness, going home. Max had scarcely spoken since the journey began. Kathryn rested her aching head on the back of the seat and closed her eyes.

Somehow, after Jon had left her, she had calmed down, tidied herself and gone to find Max. He had been talking to Annette. Her hand was on his arm and his eyes were secretly amused as he watched her looking at him. It occurred to Kathryn, as she waited for a break in their conversation, that Annette was not finding him the willing victim she had anticipated.

Kathryn asked Max to take her home. As she spoke to him, Jon came out of the kitchen, but she had found she could not meet his eyes. She had told Annette she was sorry, but she was not feeling well and supposed she had not completely recovered from her cold. Annette had agreed she looked ill, and urged Max, 'Come back to the party afterwards, won't you?' Her eyes searched his. 'We must get to know each other better.'

The car came to a standstill in the roadway outside Kathryn's house. The sound of the engine died away and there was silence. Max put his arm round her, drew her head to his shoulder.

'Well, sweet, going to tell me about it?'

'Oh, Max.' She pressed her face against him, and the tears began again. 'I wish I knew what to do!' She sobbed and he held her tightly.

'Come on, mop up.' He pushed his handkerchief into her hand. 'Now tell me.'

'It's Jon, Max. He thinks the most awful things about me.'

'Does it matter, sweet? Personally, his opinion means nothing to me.'

'Max, there's something you ought to know. I did promise not to tell anyone, but I think you deserve an explanation. I've never told you my proper surname, have I? It's Wright, Mrs. Jon Wright.'

She waited for the reaction. When it came, after a pause, it was very quiet. 'Ex-wife of—Jon Wright? For whom you work, and who lives in your house? But, Kathryn, my sweet, why on earth didn't you tell me?'

'Because Jon didn't want anyone to know. Not even your father knows yet.'

'And all these weeks you've been in close contact with the man, day in and day out, with this secret between you?' He rested his cheek against her hair. 'And you—still loving him? Am I right?'

'Right. Max,' she whispered. 'I'm so sorry, because of Francis. But once I saw Jon again, I knew.'

'Why can't you remarry? What's to stop you?'

'He wouldn't hear of it. You see, our divorce was my decision. He went away for a year, then it became two years. We were so young. I thought he regretted marrying me, so I—invented another man. He wrote and told me he would do nothing to stop me divorcing him, so we broke up, but I never stopped loving him.' She dried her tears. 'Now he thinks the worst of me. Thinks my morals are worthless.'

'And every time he's seen us together, I've made it worse for you. I've goaded and provoked him, deliberately misled him about our relationship. I suppose the last straw for you was this evening?'

'This evening was terrible, Max.' She drew a breath on a sob, and his arm tightened around her. They sat in silence. A car approached from behind them, its dazzling headlamps flood-lighting the little sports car. Then it swung round them and came to rest in the drive.

'That's Jon,' Kathryn whispered. 'Now he really will think the worst.' Tears flowed again. 'Max, I think I've come to the end of my endurance. I don't know what to do.'

'Something will work out, beautiful. May I tell you something? Just tell you once, then you must forget it? I'm in love with you, sweet. Haven't you guessed? It's ironic. You're the only woman I've met I want to marry, and you don't want me.'

'Oh, Max, what can I say?' She moved away from him, but he pulled her back.

'Say nothing, beautiful, nothing at all. But I had to tell you. I think my father has guessed, although he's said nothing to me.' He sighed. 'It's a problem, and I don't quite know the answer.'

'I must go in. Although I don't know how I'm going to face Jon. Geoff isn't home yet. Max, can I ask a favour?' She sat up and looked at him in the glow of the street lamp. 'When you go back to the party, would you bring Geoff and Helen home? Now Jon's come back early, they won't have transport.'

'Anything you say, sweet. May I kiss you goodnight?' Max asked her.

Kathryn held up her face, and he kissed her gently. 'Don't cry any more. We'll think of something.'

'Goodnight, Max. I'll be round in the morning to look after your father. Whatever the outcome of my friendship with him, that's something I must do.'

'Right, sweet.' She got out and he called, 'I'll pick you up about eleven.' He saluted and was on his way.

Kathryn let herself in the front door. There was no sign of Jon, but his dog came scurrying down the stairs to greet her. She flung her handbag down and threw her arms round his neck. He sat on his haunches and wagged his tail, and she rested her cheek against his fur. 'Hallo, Flop,' she whispered. 'You're a beautiful dog. So affectionate and loving and uncomplicated.'

His tail wagged faster and she stroked his head. She was so absorbed she did not see the figure on the landing stare down angrily, open his mouth to call the dog back, then close it abruptly.

'You'd better go back, Flop,' he heard her say. 'Your master won't want you to stay down here with me. He doesn't like me, Flop.'

She hid her face against him for a few seconds and he tried to lick her hand. She picked up her handbag, gave him a little push towards the stairs and went to bed.

She awoke early and put on her slacks and sweater, deciding that she could cope better at Francis' house in casual clothes. She went up to Geoff, her heart thumping in case she saw Jon. As she reached the landing, he came out of his kitchen. His expression was remote and cold and as their eyes met, he looked through her. They might have been strangers. She groped for Geoff's door-handle and stepped into his room as if it were a sanctuary.

Geoff looked up. 'What's the matter? Seen a ghost?'

'No. Only Jon.'

He put down his book. 'Why did you leave early last night?

159

There was some mystery. Max seemed to know all about it, but he wouldn't tell us. Jon went off, too.'

'Don't ask me about it now, Geoff. I'll tell you some other time. I'm going to look after Francis. He's caught my cold, so I must go to him. Geoff. it's only right.'

Her brother shrugged carelessly. 'If you feel that way . . .'

'I've left some cold meat in the fridge. There's jelly and cream there, too. Think you can manage lunch?'

'Don't worry about me. I'll probably go to Helen's. Her mother said I could go there any time.'

So Kathryn spent the day looking after her fiancé. He had a slight temperature and she made him stay in bed. She tidied up and cooked the lunch because his housekeeper was away that weekend. The house was very quiet. Max was out for much of the day, and Francis slept most of the time.

When he awoke, he told her he felt better, then he immediately started sneezing. Kathryn said she had expected that to happen.

'I'll be better by Tuesday, my dear. I'm sure I'll be fit enough to go to the conference with you. If not, you must go. You need a break.'

'I wouldn't go without you, Francis.'

'I insist that you go, my dear. There is no reason why you should not.'

Kathryn could think of many reasons why she should not, but she could tell her fiancé none of them. Max returned in the early evening and took her home. Kathryn had offered to go back the following day, but Francis told her he would not trouble her. His housekeeper would be back by then. He did tell her though, to let Dr. Wright know that he would not be in to the college and would he please take over as acting principal for the day. She promised to tell him. Gently she leaned down to kiss her fiancé goodbye. His eyes brightened at her action and he clung to her hand for a moment.

'Thank you, my dear, for being so good to me today. I have appreciated it greatly.'

With tears in her eyes for his gratitude, she left him.

Kathryn was dreading her first meeting with Jon next morning. When he summoned her into his office, she was afraid. She feared his anger, his sarcasm, his mistrust. She made a great

160

effort to control her feelings, pushed all thoughts of the party to the back of her mind, and braved him in his room.

As she lifted her eyes and looked at him, she gripped the back of her chair. The building was spinning like a space ship out of control, because he was smiling at her. He was actually smiling. That he was formal and even a little distant in his manner all day did not matter. He had smiled. As long as he did not insult her, criticise her or shout at her, she did not mind.

He accepted his position as acting principal for the day with equanimity, and took in his stride the extra work which came his way.

He reminded her that the conference was due to start at Buxton the next day, and told her the time of the train they would be catching.

'Will the principal be fit enough to attend?'

'He's hoping so. But if not, he—insists I go. I told him I would stay behind, but he wouldn't have it.'

Jon shrugged noncommittally. 'It's up to you.'

That evening she phoned Francis, but it was Max who answered.

'How's the patient?' she asked.

'Getting on, thanks. Still hoping to make it tomorrow. Says he'll meet you at the station, and wants to know the time of the train.'

She told him. 'Give him my love, will you, Max, and say I hope he'll soon be better.'

'If you say so, sweet. How are things with you?'

She lowered her voice. 'A little better, Max. Nothing like so bad as I anticipated.'

'I'm glad to hear that. Very glad indeed. Goodnight, sweet.'

' 'Night, Max.'

She packed her case and went upstairs to talk to Geoff. Jon was with him, and he was asking Geoff to look after Flop while he was away. As soon as Kathryn appeared, Jon left them. Geoff promised his sister to look after the house, and told her that Helen would feed him and the dog every evening. Kathryn told him she thought the dog was more important, and her brother chased her downstairs.

Kathryn stood on the platform beside the train. She turned up her fur collar and hid her cheeks from the early morning

161

chill. The hands of the station clock were moving perilously near to the time of the train's departure. Jon had given her a lift to the station. Geoff had gone with them and had driven Jon's car home.

She had no idea where Jon had gone. He had left her, saying he would travel with his friends.

Five minutes before the train was due to leave, she saw Max buy a platform ticket and hurry through the barrier towards her.

'Sorry, sweet,' he panted, 'it's been one mad rush. Father can't make it. He got up this morning, then decided he couldn't face the journey. He insists that you go, says the change will do you good.'

'I'd rather not, Max.' She picked up her case, intending to follow him out.

'You must, Kathryn. You'll only upset him if you don't. Go on, sweet, you need the rest.' He glanced at his watch. 'I must leave you. By the way, I'm off in a couple of days. Going abroad again—part of my job. May I—may I kiss you goodbye for the last time, Kathryn?'

She held up her face. 'I don't care who's looking,' he murmured, and took her in his arms. 'Whatever you choose to do, my sweet, may you be very happy.' His kiss was lingering and warm, and it brought tears to her eyes.

'Goodbye, Max. It's been so nice knowing you.'

He helped her into the empty carriage, lifted her case on to the luggage rack and with a brief wave of the hand was gone.

A few minutes later, the train jerked forward and slowly made its way out of the station. Kathryn sat in a corner seat, glad to be alone. She idly watched the town give way to the countryside, and eventually the swaying of the carriage made her close her eyes. She doubted if she would enjoy the trip. She wondered where Jon was, and what his friends were like. She knew she would see very little of him, because he was, after all, one of the organisers of the conference, as well as one of the speakers.

She was so absorbed in her thoughts that it took her some time to realise that another person had entered the carriage. At last she opened her eyes, and was startled to see Jon idly watching her from the opposite seat.

'Hallo,' he smiled. 'Where's Francis?'

'He didn't feel well enough to come.'

'So you're all alone? No wonder you look like a little girl lost. Do you like being on your own, or would you like to join me? I'm with my friends in the next coach.' Her eyes gave him his answer. 'Come along.' He pulled her up, and slid her case from the luggage rack. 'Follow me.'

They went along the swaying corridor and through to the next coach. He manipulated the sliding door and stood back to allow her to enter the compartment.

'I've found what I was looking for,' he told his friends ushering Kathryn into the carriage.

She had a fleeting impression of two rows of masculine faces. Then the pleasant face of a woman emerged from the blur before her eyes.

'Come and sit next to me, my dear,' the woman invited, moving along the seat. 'We're all friends here. We've occupied the whole carriage, so no one else can get in.'

'Thank you very much.' Kathryn squeezed herself into the small space.

'Introduce us, Jon. Don't keep us in suspense.'

So Jon introduced her. 'An old friend of mine, Miss Kathryn Swale.'

Then she learned their names.

'I'm Betty Woods, wife of Bob Woods, the man with glasses and no hair over there in the corner.'

They all laughed at the description she gave of her husband, except, of course, her husband. He was a little put out.

'It's the worry of you and the kids that's deprived me of my hair, love,' he chided her. And they laughed again.

She saw Jon watching as the colour crept back into her cheeks and the light flecked her eyes. They were all so pleasant, she thought.

'Are you one of these clever physicists, Miss Swale?' Betty Woods asked interestedly.

'Oh no. I'm a complete ignoramus where science is concerned. I'm just going because . . .'

'Because I couldn't bear to be parted from her for four days, so I brought her along with me,' Jon joked.

'So that's how the land lies, is it?' said a man called Tom Bradford. 'If that's the case, why not be nearer still to her? Come and sit next to him, Miss Swale. Look, Bob, you go and sit beside your wife,' Bob pretended to groan, 'then Jon's lady love can come and sit next to him.'

'Oh, please don't disturb anybody,' Kathryn urged, looking embarrassed. 'It really doesn't matter.'

'Come along, Kathryn.' Jon was obviously enjoying himself. 'Take the gentleman up on his kind offer,' and he made room for her. She lowered herself reluctantly into the small gap.

'Go on, Jon,' Tom Bradford urged, 'put your arm where it ought to be. Then it won't get squashed.'

Jon looked at her enquiringly. 'May I?'

'Listen to him,' laughed a man called Bill. 'He's asking permission! Never do that, boy, the lady might say no.'

Kathryn nodded. 'It looks as if you'll have to, Jon.'

So he slid his arm round her back and held her shoulder.

Betty woods looked at them, and was satisfied. 'There, now they're comfy.'

Bob Woods smiled affectionately at his wife. 'There she goes. My wife is always matchmaking.'

'Don't do that,' Jon pretended to be upset. 'It might have the opposite effect and scare the lady off.'

His grip on her shoulder tightened and he whispered, 'Sorry about this. I never thought they'd take me seriously.'

'Can't be helped,' she whispered back.

'Now they're murmuring sweet nothings,' Bill chortled. 'You know, Jon, we've known you quite a while, and it's high time you settled down. At your age you ought to have a wife and six kids.'

'Then I'd be bald like friend Bob here.' Jon raised a hand to his head. 'No, I think I'll stay as I am and keep my hair.'

Later they became serious and discussed the coming conference. As Kathryn listened, she discovered that underneath their banter they were serious, knowledgeable men, enthusiastic about their subjects and vigorous in their exchange of ideas.

Betty stopped knitting and leaned across to Kathryn. 'I'm going for the rest, too. You and I must keep together, dear, it'll be nice having someone on my intellectual level to talk to!'

Kathryn laughed and said she would love to stay with her. Still Jon did not remove his arm. In fact, he seemed to settle it even more securely round her.

The dining-car attendant appeared and they ordered morning coffee. Jon and Kathryn shared a tray on their laps. They laughed when the swaying of the carriage made them spill the coffee, they laughed when the biscuits got damp, they laughed at all the things which, at other times, would have made them despair.

'It's so obvious they're in love,' Betty commented. 'They're giggling at everything. How nice to be in that state.'

'You're quite wrong, you know,' Jon told them, 'quite wrong.'

'Don't you believe it,' Tom jeered. 'You can't fool us.'

'Can't we?' Jon raised his eyebrows and smiled at Kathryn, and she smiled back at him.

The hotel was large and imposing and built of grey stone. The Turrets, it was called, and the towers and turrets which were the essence of its design gave it the appearance of an impregnable castle. The amenities it offered, however, were superior by far to those found in any ancient fortress, and the room to which Jon carried Kathryn's case was the last word in comfort. Jon looked around approvingly, told her that his room was next door but one, and that if she required any help, she would probably find him there. He left her, saying vaguely that he would see her around.

She felt lost when he had gone, wanting him back as soon as he had closed her door. She washed and found her way down to the dining-room where lunch was awaiting them. She felt confused by the mass of white table coverings and glinting cutlery, and when her eyes cleared, searched for Jon. He was seated at a table for six and it was fully occupied. She floundered and was about to turn away when Betty Woods saw her.

'Miss Swale,' she called, 'I've saved a place for you. I've lost my husband and it looks as if you've lost your Jon.'

Indescribably grateful, Kathryn took her place next to Betty, who introduced her to the others at the table. Gradually, Kathryn sorted out her companions. On her left was a smart young woman wearing attractive blue-rimmed glasses.

'Are you one of us?' she asked Kathryn.

'No, Vivienne,' Betty leaned forward and answered her. 'She's one of me, a non-scientist, here for the rest.'

'Have you come alone?' Vivienne persisted.

'No, she's with Jon Wright. She's a friend of his, aren't you, Miss Swale?'

'Yes, and please call me Kathryn.'

'I'm Betty, and this is Vivienne Gray, another of those clever scientists.'

'So you're Jon's friend, are you?' The young woman's interest was intense. 'And where did you meet our Jon?'

Kathryn countered that with another question. 'You know him, then?'

'Everyone knows Dr. Wright. He's the brains behind this annual conference.'

'He's a bright boy, Kathryn, don't doubt that.' Betty looked across at him. 'Some call him brilliant. He's written a couple of textbooks on physics, didn't you know? But then,' she added with a little smile, 'I don't suppose you discuss that sort of thing when you're together.'

Vivienne looked curiously at Kathryn's ring. 'I see you're engaged. When are you and Jon getting married?'

Greatly embárrassed, Kathryn hid her left hand in her lap. 'Oh, I—I don't know about that . . .'

Betty came to her rescue, as the waiter lowered their first course in front of them. 'They're both very reluctant to talk about it. It's a big secret, apparently.'

After that, conversation veered away from personal matters, and her companions joined in the general discussion. As the meal proceeded, Kathryn stole a look now and then at Jon. He seemed to have forgotten her presence. He was deep in conversation with a beautiful young woman on one side of him, and a bespectacled man on his other. That the young woman was interested in him as a man, as well as a physicist, was obvious to any observer. Whether he returned the interest was harder to discover.

'What are you doing this afternoon, Kathryn?' Betty asked, when they were drinking their coffee. 'There's an afternoon session of the conference until five o'clock, then they disperse and reassemble for dinner, and that's followed by a sort of social gathering. Most of the men talk shop, unless their wives stop them! After lunch, I'm off to have a look at the town. Would you like to come with me?'

'I'd love to, Betty.'

At this point, Vivienne excused herself and walked across to Jon's table. She said something and they all looked round at Kathryn, who pretended to ignore their interest.

166

'Oh dear,' she thought, 'if they keep linking my name with Jon's, he'll begin to regret I've come.'

Betty interrupted her thoughts. 'You see that attractive young woman next to Jon? You wouldn't think that she's a physicist, too, would you? She's head of the science department at a large girls' school in the Midlands. She's been working hard on Jon for months trying to get him interested in more than her brains, my dear. But she's had no luck so far, although they speak the same language, as it were. And that young woman over there with the red hair—she's a mathematician. She's been after him for a long time. She used to work in the same firm as Jon. He took her out a few times, but there it ended, much to her chagrin. I could point out half a dozen women in this room who'd give their all to catch him—clever young women, all on his intellectual plane. He's just not interested. I may sound a bit catty, but it's the truth. We've all watched from the sidelines.'

Kathryn's astonishment increased with every word she spoke. Where, then, were all the girl-friends he delighted in flaunting in front of her when he was at his most provocative? If he was as resistant to the opposite sex as Betty would have her believe, then many of his 'lady-friends' must have been largely mythical. And where did Annette fit into this picture?

Betty was saying, 'Now perhaps you'll understand why we were so curious about you. He's kept you very quiet. Have you known him long?'

'Oh—er—a short while. He—works in the same technical college as I do. He's a head of department.'

'I know he recently changed his job. So that's where you met him. It's early days yet, then. I suppose that's why you're both so shy about it. Are you a teacher, by the way?'

'No. I'm—on the administrative staff.'

At this point, people began to drift out of the dining-room for the afternoon session.

'They're off to the conference hall,' Betty said. 'I suppose we'd better be on our way, too.'

Jon came across to them. 'What will you do, Kathryn?'

'Oh, she's coming with me, Jon. I'll take care of her for you.'

Kathryn looked at him a little shyly, and he smiled at her.

'See you later, then.' He raised his hand briefly and rejoined his colleagues.

Kathryn had a pleasant afternoon with her new-found friend. They window-shopped, and bought souvenirs and gifts for relatives and acquaintances. They had tea at a picturesque tea shop in a side street and arrived back at the hotel in advance of the conference party.

There was time for a quick bath, Kathryn decided, before the demand on the bathrooms became too great. Then she changed for dinner. She wore her deep pink dress and its colour was an excellent foil for her diamond brooch. She put on her make-up and brushed her hair and sat for a while on the windowseat, gazing out at the hills around the town. The view was one she would remember for a long time, and in that cool spring evening, the summits shone brightly in the declining sun.

Before she left her room, she had made up her mind to remove the cause of her embarrassment—and Jon's. She slipped her engagement ring from her finger and put it carefully away. That would stop the speculation about her friendship with Jon.

She decided to take the plunge and descend to the hotel lounge. She stood in the doorway feeling forlorn because Jon was nowhere to be seen. Betty was beside her husband, talking animatedly to another guest. Vivienne was deep in conversation with a colleague.

Kathryn turned quickly and walked towards the stairs. Jon was coming down them. 'Where are you going?' he demanded.

'Back to my room.'

'I've just been up there looking for you. Do you want something from your room?'

'No.'

'Then why go up there?'

'I—I don't know anyone, so I . . .'

'Ran away, is that it?' He grasped her arm. 'You'd better stay with me. Can't have you looking as lost and lonely as that. You're supposed to be enjoying yourself.'

They walked together to the lounge and a number of eyes swung round and subjected them to intense scrutiny.

'Come over here, Kathryn. There are a number of people who want to meet the "friend" I've brought with me.'

She was introduced to many faces and promptly forgot the names attached to them, but it didn't seem to matter. They were all so friendly, Jon bought her a drink, and they toasted each other.

One of the men nudged his neighbour. 'Won't be long now, Frank, before our Jon is a family man, like the rest of us. Must say,' he whispered loudly behind his hand, 'I approve of his choice, although it's taken him long enough to make up his mind.'

Frank nodded. 'There'll be a lot of broken girlish hearts in this room, old boy, once it gets around that young Doc Wright's caught at last.'

Jon laughed and shook his head helplessly. 'It's no good putting two and two together and making five. I've been immune to feminine wiles for years and I still am. I haven't been caught, as you put it. I'm still a free agent.' He looked down at Kathryn. 'We're just friends, aren't we, Kathryn?'

'M'mm.' She smiled up at him. 'Just very good friends.'

He took a swift breath as the others laughed heartily. 'That caught you on the hop, Doctor Jon,' Frank commented appreciatively.

She knew she had annoyed him by the way his eyes darkened as they regarded her, but she merely grinned at him. He didn't throw her overboard after that as she thought he might. Instead he kept her with him as he moved from group to group, taking her hand and pulling her behind him. He introduced her to all his acquaintances as his 'friend', and their faces wore the same expression of concentrated curiosity as all the others when they looked her over.

As she watched them watching her, the ghost of an idea crept stealthily into her consciousness and began to haunt her. Was he using her as a shield against all the pursuing young women around him? If they accepted she was his future wife, they would not trouble him again with their attentions.

She noticed the respect with which his colleagues treated him, and how they deferred to his opinion and turned to him for advice.

'You're dining with me tonight, Kathryn,' he told her as the dinner gong resounded throughout the hotel. He led her to the table and as they took their places, he asked how she had spent the afternoon. He listened with interest to her answer and said he was delighted to hear that she and Betty got on so well together. Then he turned from her and launched into a animated technical discussion with a colleague, appearing to forget about her. But Kathryn was happy just to be at his side.

169

When the meal ended, they moved to a private lounge and the social evening began. As Betty had warned her, they did little more than talk. and it was mostly shop. She stayed at Jon's side for a while. then wandered away—he didn't even notice she had gone—and found Betty, who immediately made a place for her at her side.

'Lost him again? I don't know where Bob is either. They get so absorbed in their discussions they forget we even exist.'

Betty invited her to explore the rest of the town with her next day. 'I want to see the parks and climb the hills to look at the view. I'd like to visit the museum, too. We could have lunch out somewhere.'

Kathryn was delighted with the idea, and they arranged to meet straight after breakfast. She excused herself then. saying it was getting late and she was tired. She looked round for Jon. and saw that he was in the centre of a circle of friends having what appeared to be a lively argument. Not wishing to disturb him, she went to bed without saying goodnight to him.

She was up early next morning. The blue sky and the scent of spring drew her outside before breakfast, and she took a brisk walk round the extensive grounds of the hotel. She ran up the steps and into the hotel entrance foyer flushed and tingling with the exercise.

Jon was looking out for her. He seemed irritated. 'Where have you been? I went to your room and again you were missing.'

'I went for a walk. It's lovely out there.'

'If you'd asked me, I would have gone with you.' He sounded peeved. 'And where did you get to last night?'

'I went to bed. Why?'

'You might have told me. You didn't even say goodnight.' he grumbled away at her.

'You seemed so absorbed in your discussion, I didn't like to disturb you.'

He grunted. 'Well, come on, breakfast's being served.'

He led her into the dining-room and again he sat beside her. She looked round at Betty, and they waved.

She told Jon, 'I'm spending the day with Betty. We're going sightseeing.'

'Don't get lost,' was all he said.

When breakfast was over, he left her, saying 'I'll see you for

170

dinner this evening,' and Kathryn experienced a quicksilver flick of pleasure at the thought.

She had a wonderful day with Betty. They walked, they climbed, they sat in the park. They almost talked themselves into visiting the Baths, but held back at the last moment.

'We're not that old or rheumaticky yet, are we?' Betty laughed.

They returned to the hotel tired but satisfied with the happy day they had spent together.

Kathryn asked Jon that evening when he would be addressing the conference.

'Friday morning.' He smiled. 'Why, do you want to hear me?'

Betty was sitting with them, and joined in. 'Of course she wants to hear you. It's only natural. However bad you may be, she'll think you're wonderful!'

'Well, you've got a ticket you've never used. Remind me to take you with me on Friday. You going, Betty?'

'Might as well. I've got a ticket, too.'

Jon saw her up to her room that night. 'Kathryn, tomorrow afternoon and evening are free of discussions and talks. Would you care to spend the time with me? If not, just say so.'

His unusual diffidence touched her. 'I'd love to, Jon.'

'I thought of visiting the Pavilion Gardens. I've caught a tantalising glimpse of them each time I've gone to the conference hall. I'd like to see them properly. It's a date, then?'

She nodded. They looked at each other for a quiet moment.

'Well, goodnight, Kathy.'

'Goodnight, Jon.' He turned at the door, smiled and left her.

They were lucky with the weather that afternoon. It was warm and bright and they wandered along the paths between the lawns and under the trees struggling into bud. They stopped at the children's corner and watched the young ones at play.

Somehow their hands touched and held, their fingers entwined. It seemed so natural they scarcely noticed at first. Then Kathryn became conscious of what had happened. She looked at Jon, expecting him to pull his hand away, but he didn't. He seemed to Kathryn to have thrown off the years. As they meandered along, he was more relaxed than she had ever seen him. His eyes when he looked at her held an odd sort of light she had never seen in them before. Her heart beat faster.

'Let's sit down somewhere, Kathryn. The brisk pace we've sustained has tired me out!'

They found a place on the grass a short distance from the path, and Jon spread out his coat for them to sit on. After a while, Kathryn lay back and pillowed her head on her hands. The cries of the children at play, the hum of the occasional aircraft flying over the park, the incessant bird-song, all merged and she had to hold herself back from slipping into sleep. Jon was with her, and she was content.

'Who are you dreaming of, Kathy? Max?'

Jon had moved to her side and had propped himself on his elbow.

She came out of her dream with a start. 'Why? Should I be?'

'I can think of no one else.' He lowered his voice. 'He's in love with you, you know.'

She turned her head away. 'I know. He told me.'

'Aren't you pleased? After all, most women are happy when they discover the man they love loves them.'

'Yes,' she answered indifferently. 'I suppose they are.'

He was silent for a while. Then, 'Why did you take off your engagement ring, Kathy?'

'They kept asking me if I was engaged to you. So I took it off.'

'Do you hate me so much?'

'No. I just didn't want to embarrass you by burdening you with a fiancée you didn't want.'

There was a long pause and Kathryn did not dare to look at him.

At last he spoke, and the world rocked around her. 'Just as, nearly ten years ago, you didn't want to burden me with a wife I didn't want?'

Her head shot round. 'How did you know that? Has Geoff been talking to you?'

'No.' He was smiling like a man who had just found the answer to a tantalising and deeply complex problem. 'I just used the method by which so many important scientific discoveries are made—by an inspired guess, a shot in the dark.'

He lay back on the grass with a sigh of contentment. Seconds

172

later, he propped himself up again and looked about him. 'Watching all these couples around us, wrapped up in their love, brings home to me what the expression "spring fever" means.' He hovered over her and she opened her eyes and looked directly into his, only inches away.

'It's catching, Kathy. I've caught it. Shall I pass it on to you?'

So slowly and so purposefully, his lips descended and for a long, ecstatic moment, rested on hers. He raised his head at last and the light in his eyes dazzled her. 'Now you kiss me,' he whispered. 'Kiss me back, Kathy.'

She found she was powerless to resist his urgency. Shyly, she raised her hands and rested them on the back of his head. Then she exerted some pressure and his mouth moved towards hers. She kissed him.

Overcome, she rolled away and closed her eyes. When she found sufficient courage to look at him, he was gazing at her with an expression which made her heart race.

'I think it's time we went, don't you?' He smiled, stood up and held out his hand to her. 'Coming?'

He put on his coat and they wandered hand in hand towards the park gates. On the way they passed a kiosk and Jon bought ice creams. They sat on a bench and ate them.

'We're not the only ones here from the conference group,' Jon remarked, looking round. 'I've seen a lot of people I know while we've been here this afternoon.'

As she listened to his words, spring changed to winter in her heart. She became tormented with doubt, haunted by the ghost she had no power to exorcise. 'Were any of them the women you are running away from?' she desperately wanted to ask him. 'And is that why you kissed me?'

She wanted to cry. How could she give away her feelings for him as she had done today, she chided herself, when he was using her merely as a protection from unwanted female attentions?

They returned to the hotel and parted in the entrance foyer.

'I'm going to change for dinner, Jon.'

He released her hand at last and she went up to her room.

Jon saw her as soon as she appeared in the lounge doorway. He went to her, his hand extended. 'Come on in, shy one.'

'We saw you in the park, Jon,' Tom Bradford called as they passed him, a knowing gleam in his eye.

'So did we,' Betty echoed, equally knowingly. 'Now you can't deny it any longer, can you? Don't try to pretend there's nothing between you.'

Jon appeared to capitulate. 'All right, all right,' His arm encircled Kathryn's waist. 'I give in. We're in love.' He whispered into her ear. 'Come on, Kathy, act for all you're worth. Let's give them their money's worth. They've been waiting for this for a long time.'

She smiled into his eyes. She did not have to act even if he did, but she could not tell him that. She raised her arm and put it round his waist. They walked thus across the lounge to the couch which others had vacated for them. The young women stared.

'They're green-eyed,' Kathryn thought incongruously. 'If only they knew the truth!'

They sat side by side and hand in hand. Someone said, 'This calls for a drink. This is really something to celebrate. Our Jon's caught at last '

'Ah, but,' Jon held up his hand, 'I'm not married yet. There's many a slip.'

Nobody believed him.

There were drinks all round and everyone toasted the happy couple, as they called them.

'Look, chaps ' Jon appeared at last to be getting worried at the extent of his involvement, 'I'm not even engaged yet. Give me a chance! The lady might say no.'

'Not judging by the look on her face,' they laughed.

Jon glanced at the girl beside him. 'You're doing well,' he whispered 'So well, in fact, you could almost fool me!'

When dinner was over, Jon murmured in her ear, 'Will you come for a walk, Kathy? Nobody will mind. In fact, they'll expect it.'

She agreed and ran upstairs for her coat.

Hand in hand they went into the darkness and Kathryn immediately removed her hand from Jon's. She huddled into her coat and thrust her hands into her pockets. She started shivering and she knew that it was not entirely the cool night air which was causing her to shake.

'Cold?' Jon asked.

174

'A bit.'

'If you'll cuddle up to me, I'll keep you warm.' His arm went round her.

'There's no need to pretend now, Jon,' she said stiffly. 'Nobody's looking.'

He said nothing and his arm stayed where it was.

'Sorry to get you mixed up in all this. Had no idea it would reach such proportions. Never mind, after lunch-time tomorrow the conference ends. Then we can drop all pretence and go back to normal. Will that please you?'

This time it was Kathryn who was silent.

'After the conference, I'm going to Manchester to visit my sister and her family. Did you know, Kathryn?'

Her heart sank. 'So you won't be travelling home with me?'

'No. Pleased?'

She did not answer.

They walked on through the dark streets, passing the houses, shops and ornamental gardens without being conscious that they were doing so.

'Kathy, tell me. When I left you all those years ago, and you decided to break with me, what did you do?'

'Oh, let me think. It's a long time back. I went on working. I had to earn enough to get Geoff through his studies. Gran took in more lodgers. We just about scraped by.'

Jon looked round, stopped and said, 'Do you know, I believe we're lost.'

'That will amuse them back at the hotel. They'll say it's part of the complaint.' They laughed together.

'We'll just have to turn round and ask the way back.'

So they did. When they eventually walked into the hotel, looking dazed by the bright lights within, they were holding hands again, and some of the stars in the sky seemed to have fallen into their eyes.

'We got lost,' Jon told them.

Kathryn knew he was playing to the gallery, but she joined in wholeheartedly.

'Yes, and it was wonderful,' she added, and they all laughed.

She took her coat up to her bedroom, then returned to the lounge, and was given a place of honour next to Jon, near the roaring fire. As his arm slipped round her, she lowered her head to his shoulder, knowing how convincing they looked, especially when Jon's cheek rubbed against her hair. She looked up at him and he dropped a kiss on her forehead.

The assembled company loved it, and by their silent appreciation, asked for more. She expected him to whisper to her not to overdo it, but he didn't. Instead, he murmured, 'Keep it going, sweetheart, they're lapping it up.'

Colour swamped her cheeks at the term of endearment, which must have slipped out unintentionally. No one had noticed her embarrassment as the talk had veered to the conference again, and Jon joined in. This time she was content to listen. Sitting by his side in the circle of his arm, she felt she could not ask for more.

As the evening progressed, late tea was served, after which people began to drift upstairs to bed. Kathryn tried to stifle a yawn, because she did not want to break the magic spell of this pretended love. But Jon had noticed and asked her if she wanted to go to bed. She nodded and he pulled her from the couch. His hand grasped hers as they walked towards the stairs.

'My word ' someone said, 'they've got it bad, haven't they?'

'See you in the morning, Kathryn,' Betty called to her. 'Don't forget we're going to do some hard listening at the conference hall tomorrow.'

Kathryn found her key and opened her bedroom door. She turned to face him, making her expression completely blank.

'Goodnight, Jon.' She started to retreat into the room, when he took her hand and tried to pull her towards him. She resisted.

'No need to pretend now, Jon.'

'But, Kathy——' He stopped, lifted his shoulders, then they drooped. 'Oh well, goodnight.'

He walked briskly along to his bedroom door, unlocked it and went in.

Kathryn did not turn on her light. She walked to the window and stared into the darkness for a long time, her eyes blurred with tears.

Kathryn and Betty found the final session of the conference interesting despite the fact that they understood very little of what was going on. Jon spoke well and convincingly, and to judge by the reaction of the learned audience, he spoke with accuracy and authority. Their applause echoed throughout the

176

conference hall, and Kathryn found herself clapping too, although she had hardly understood a word of it.

Betty laughed at her enthusiasm. 'I shall begin to think you're one of Them in disguise if you applaud like that. I'll bet you understood as much as I did, which was precisely nothing.'

Kathryn nodded. 'Nothing at all. But I'm sure Jon was wonderful!'

After lunch, Jon insisted on settling Kathryn's hotel bill and accompanied her to the station. She was travelling south with Betty and her husband.

'Have a nice weekend,' she told him, as they stood outside the railway carriage 'You'll be back at the college—when?'

'Monday afternoon. I've got extended leave of absence until then.'

'I'll do whatever I can to clear some of the work in the morning.'

His smile was mocking. 'Thank you, Miss Swale. I always did say you were a first-class secretary. Don't know what I'd do without you.' He put a finger under her chin and tilted her face upwards.

The others called to them. 'Come on, you two love-birds. You'll have to tear yourselves apart now. Say goodbye. We're off in a couple of minutes.'

'Well, this is it, Kathy. Goodbye till Monday. I shall have to kiss you, I'm afraid Never mind, last time.'

She went into his arms and their kiss seemed never-ending. Tears were in her eyes when they parted.

'Real ones?' he whispered, as he touched them with his finger. 'Or crocodile? If so, you're a better actress than I thought!'

'Goodbye, Jon.'

She got into the carriage and leaned out of the window. As the train moved away and gathered speed, he stood on the platform and waved. The wheels screeched and squealed as if in pain, taking her irrevocably from him, and he grew progressively smaller until his figure disappeared altogether from sight.

CHAPTER XIII

KATHRYN arrived home tired and dispirited, afraid to count the hours that must pass before she would see Jon again. It seemed a lifetime until Monday. She went upstairs and told Geoff about her trip to Buxton, leaving out the episode of her short-lived 'engagement'. That was a story too precious to be told.

After her brother had gone to Helen's for the evening, Kathryn knew, with a sinking heart, that she must fulfil her promise and telephone Francis. Her feet dragged as she crossed the hall and her arm was weighted with reluctance as she lifted the receiver.

She dialled his number.

'Francis? Kathryn here.'

'How are you, my dear? Did you enjoy your little break?'

'Very much, thank you, Francis. I feel better for it.'

'Have you just got home?'

'Well, I've had some tea.'

'I shall be going out in a few minutes. I've been invited to spend the evening at George Creswell's house. I did explain that I thought you might be too tired to accompany me. Was I right, or would you like to come?'

'Oh no, Francis,' she hastened to assure him. 'I would certainly be much too tired. I'm glad you explained.'

'I doubt if I shall be seeing you before Monday, Kathryn. I'm going to my brother's for the weekend. He and his wife live in Surrey, you may remember. He invited me some time ago, and I thought I would take him up on his offer. Felt I could do with a change, you know, after that cold.'

'What a good idea, Francis. The rest should do you good. Have a nice time, won't you?'

'I will, my dear. Thank you for ringing. Goodbye, now.'

'Goodbye, Francis.' Slowly she replaced the receiver.

She felt she had to sit down. She found her way to the armchair by the empty fireplace. Now she knew she must face up to her innermost doubts, the secret uncertainties she had so

178

securely locked away. Relentlessly she took them out and examined them one by one and knew with absolute conviction that she could never, under any circumstances, marry Francis Rutland.

She fingered the watch he had given her, she pulled at his ring and wanted to tear them off and fling them away from her. She knew then what she must do on Monday morning, while Jon was away. She would go to Francis and tell him of her decision. She would say she was sorry, and that she hoped he would understand.

How, she wondered, would Jon take the news of her broken engagement? Her heart raced as she pictured his reaction, but as her imagination began to break through reality and batter frenziedly on the doors of Paradise, she placed a strict embargo on such thoughts, and turned instead to counting the hours until Jon's return. The weekend passed thus with surprising speed.

Now it was Sunday night, and she was drifting into sleep when the front door opened. She stirred into wakefulness. Was she dreaming or had she really heard Jon's voice? Judging by the scuffling and yelping and the patter of paws on the stairs, she knew it must indeed be Jon. Flop was going mad with delight. He was not the only one—Kathryn could hardly contain her excitement. So Jon had come home sooner than expected. The muffled conversation of the men drifted down to her and eventually she forced herself into a state of calmness and settled down at last to a pleasant dream-encrusted sleep.

When she arrived at the college next morning, she knew with certainty that he would be in his room. She flicked a comb through her hair and added a little more lipstick. Bright eyes gazed back at her from the mirror, and she acknowledged that it was quite beyond her power to extinguish the brilliance within them before she was called into Jon's office.

She relived the moments in his arms when they had kissed goodbye on the station platform three days ago, and her heart pounded at the thought of being near him again.

The internal telephone startled her out of her dreams. And then he called to her.

'Miss Swale? Come in, please.'

Was it her imagination, or did he sound abrupt? He was

179

probably doing it to tease her, she decided, and smiled as she appeared at his door.

He did not even look up. 'Sit down.'

She tried to ignore his sharpness. 'So you came home early, Jon?'

'Yes.' Still he did not look at her.

'Did you have a nice weekend?'

'Yes. Will you please sit down?' His frown, when at last he raised his eyes from his desk, emphasised the black shadows beneath them and the unusual heaviness of his whole bearing.

She caught her breath. 'Are you well, Jon? Is there anything wrong?'

'No.' His reply was a sigh. 'There's nothing wrong, and there's no need for you to concern yourself about my state of health, as I've said before.'

Kathryn was filled with dismay. Now what had she done wrong? Overstepped the line, perhaps, giving him the impression she was chasing him? Or was this his way of telling her that as he no longer needed her as a shield from pursuing females, he was now reverting to the old mistrust and enmity?

She watched him extract a cigarette from the packet. She dared his displeasure and immediately wished she hadn't.

'Are you smoking again, Jon? You—you didn't smoke at all, did you, while we were away?'

Slowly, deliberately, he lowered his smouldering cigarette to the ash-tray, put his hands on the desk and leaned forward, his expression granite-hard.

'Look, let's get this straight, once and for all. I'm a free agent, understand? I can do what I like. As you so often reminded me while we were away, no one is looking, so there is no further need for pretence. We've returned to normal. What I do with my health and my life is my concern, not yours. So I should be obliged if, from now on, and until you leave to be married, you will regard yourself simply as my secretary, and not as my keeper, my wife, girl-friend or anything else you care to name. Have you got that?'

She paled and looked down at her notebook.

'And while we're on the subject, I might as well tell you now that as soon as it can possibly be arranged, I shall be leaving your house and moving into a furnished flat. I've had details of one through the post this morning which sounds ideal. I shall inspect it this evening, and if it's suitable, will conclude the whole transaction in as short a time as possible.'

Her eyes caught fire. 'Do I take this as a form of notice that you're quitting? What about the agreement you signed with Geoff?'

'I've already discussed that with him, and he's prepared to accept a lump sum in compensation.'

'You both did all this once again without consulting me?'

He swivelled slowly in his chair. 'I seem to remember, not so very long ago, having to talk you into accepting me into the house in the first place. Now, with typical feminine inconsistency, you are objecting to my leaving. You really can't have it both ways.'

The internal telephone rang. Kathryn made no attempt to answer it. She doubted at that moment whether she could move at all. She was paralysed with despair. She could not understand his complete change of heart. What had caused it? Something his sister had said? No, that would be too ridiculous.

Jon was speaking to Annette. 'The conference? Yes, thanks, I enjoyed it. It was a pleasant interlude.' He looked at Kathryn's bowed head. 'No, not romantic. As I've told you before,' his voice hardened, 'I never get involved, with any woman. I could come round this evening, but I'm going to look at a flat first. Sounds a possibility. Yes, you can come with me, if you like. I'll pick you up at fiveish at your office.'

He slammed the receiver down. 'Now I would like to do some work.'

But Kathryn was standing and shaking with shock and grief.

He looked up at her with some surprise.

'I'm sorry, Dr. Wright, there's a limit to what anybody can take. I've reached that limit. You will have to find someone else to act as your secretary. I shall seek another appointment.'

He gazed at his pen, turned it round and put it in his pocket. 'That is a matter for you alone to decide. I think, however, you are right. It would be better for us both if you were to go elsewhere. Our past relationship is constantly intruding into our work—creating an impossible situation between us.'

The telephone shrilled again. He answered and handed the receiver to Kathryn. 'Principal's secretary for you.'

'Yes? An appointment to see me at eleven? Yes, I suppose I

181

shall just have to make myself free.' She replaced the receiver.

'In the meantime, I wish to do some work, Miss Swale. I have a meeting at eleven at the education office.'

Somehow they got through the work. Kathryn was beyond tears, beyond feeling, beyond understanding. She took his dictation like an automaton, returned to her room, typed the letters. Jon left for his meeting.

Kathryn kept her appointment with Francis. As soon as she entered his room, she was aware of a strained atmosphere.

'Sit down, please.' He indicated a chair.

His hands were clasped together on his blotter and he seemed at a loss for words. When he spoke, his voice was rough and slow.

'On Friday evening, as you know, I visited my friend George Creswell and his wife.' He paused. Kathryn knew what was coming.

'Quite by chance, I mentioned that you had gone away for a few days. I told them where.' His eyes, heavy and dull, focussed on hers. They were slightly bloodshot, Kathryn noticed idly. 'I also told them with whom. Mrs. Creswell then said, by way of conversation, "Isn't that the man she married some years ago, and from whom she subsequently obtained a divorce?" I told her I was not aware of that fact, and she said very apologetically that she had assumed I would know all about it. Her husband told her to say no more. It was, he said, up to my fiancé to tell me the truth. I could get no more out of them. So would you please inform me, now and without delay, if what they said was correct?'

Her voice faltered. 'I'm sorry, Francis. It—it is the truth. I'm sorry also that I misled you into thinking I was a widow. I regret ever having said I was. I had every intention of telling you, please believe that. Max told me some time ago about your attitude to divorce.'

'How long were you married to your former husband?' His voice sounded strained.

'Our marriage proper lasted six months. In name, it lasted until the necessary time had elapsed for me to divorce him for desertion. He went abroad to further his studies and he—he never returned to me. If I'm to be entirely honest with you, I must tell you that I have spent the intervening years bitterly regretting my decision to divorce him.' She caught her breath. 'And

182

s things stand, I shall spend the rest of my life doing the same thing.'

She drew the ring from her finger. 'Our engagement must obviously end, Francis. To be honest, I came to that decision myself this weekend.'

As she handed him the ring, he said gruffly, 'I too have had my doubts for some time. I've seen you with Max, and this made me uncomfortably aware of the age difference between us.'

'I'll hand in my resignation, I'll leave my job, the college altogether, if you wish.'

He nodded. 'In all the circumstances, I think your only course is to resign as soon as possible, and leave after serving the usual period of notice.'

She rose and pulled the watch from her wrist. 'I would not dream of keeping this. Thank you for giving it to me. Thank you for everything, Francis. Goodbye.'

He did not reply, just sat, hands still clasped in front of him, staring down at them.

Kathryn slumped at her desk. She had suffered rejection, in the short space of one morning, at the hands of two men. She tried to sort out her thoughts, but gave up in despair. One vital fact dominated all others—she must put as much distance as quickly as possible between herself and her place of work.

Now, she would go, not tomorrow, not at the end of the month, but now. She slipped some paper into her typewriter and wrote her letter of resignation. In the letter she said that she preferred to forfeit her salary in lieu of notice. She addressed the envelope to the Chief Education Officer and decided to post it on her way home.

She dialled Jill Summers' extension. 'Jill,' she told her, 'I'm giving you advance warning that you'll be needed up here in my office from this afternoon onwards. I'm sorry about it, Jill, but I'm leaving.' She continued talking through Jill's anxious questioning. 'I can't explain, dear. I'm going, right now. Say goodbye to the others for me.'

She put on her coat, gathered together all her belongings and went along to the staff room, hoping to find Geoff. She found Helen instead.

'What's up, Kath? You look terrible.'

183

'I'm leaving, Helen.' Now the tears threatened. 'Can't tell you why. Not now. Just tell Geoff, will you?'

'Sit down, love,' Helen urged. 'Get your breath back.'

She shook her head, unable to speak. She turned and ran along the corridor and down the stairs to the entrance foyer. As she went out through the doors, she stood for a few seconds looking back at the building in which she had spent so many years of her working life. She ran to the bus stop, unable to get away fast enough.

As she entered her front door, the dog hurled himself at her legs, and she bent down and put her arms round him. In her desperately unhappy state, he was the only creature in the world from whom she could ask and receive warmth and affection. She shared her meagre lunch with him, then she went out, pushing him back into the hall as she closed the front door.

She knew what she had to do. There was a secretarial agency in the town which would supply her with details of vacancies in the offices of local firms, but to her disappointment it appeared that they had nothing for her on their books at the moment. When they heard the extent of her experience and qualifications, they assured her that something should come along soon to suit her. At her request, they gave her information about vacant secretarial posts overseas and supplied her with a pile of forms to fill in. She took these home and studied them over tea.

The hearth was black and empty of warmth, and she tried to imagine what the house, and what life itself would be like, without Jon. Although somewhere inside her there was a feeling of joy at her release from the intolerable burden which her engagement had become, her thoughts were far from happy. She had no present and she had no future. Bleak despair lay round her like a shroud and she reached down blindly to stroke the dog at her feet, gaining some sort of comfort from the warmth of his golden coat.

She wondered vaguely what time it was. The telephone rang and her move to answer it was automatic. 'Yes?' she said dully into the mouthpiece, but on hearing the caller's voice, rang off. She could not speak to anyone, least of all Jon.

Determined to remove herself as far away from his as possible, she sat at the table and read and re-read the forms which the agency had given her. Then she started writing. Name, it said. How strange, how ironic that she had to tell them it was Wright, Kathryn Wright. Married? Yes, No, of course not. Divorced. She looked for a long time at what she had written, until tears filled her eyes and she had to search for a handkerchief. She persisted with the task. Age, education, experience, salary required. Slowly and laboriously the details were committed to paper. She paused for a rest and Flop moved and put his head on her lap. Absentmindedly, she stroked him, then she rested her head on her hands, hopeless and despairing.

The dog stood up, alert at once, and scampered into the hall. It's Geoff, Kathryn thought, and did not move. But it was not Geoff. It was Jon, and he was talking to his dog. Her head jerked round as he appeared at the door. She could see he was angry and she knew then that she still had not reached the limits of misery.

He spoke. 'No doubt you considered it a joke to walk out on me without a word of warning or explanation.' He paused, but she did not respond. 'Perhaps it amused you to take literally what I said this morning about getting another job?'

She still had nothing to say.

His anger increased. 'How am I supposed to manage? How am I supposed to get through all the work which accumulated last week, without your help?'

'That's not my problem any more.' Weariness made her drag her words. 'I've left. I resigned this morning. Pressure was put upon me to do so.'

'Pressure? Not by me. It was your idea, remember, and I merely agreed with you.'

'No, it was not you. The principal intimated that it was my only course.'

'The principal? What crime have you committed that he should go to those lengths to get rid of you?'

'The crime of having been married to you. The even greater crime of being a divorced woman. He discovered the truth by accident.' She stopped, but there was no movement, no word from the listener. 'I had intended to tell him, of course. But it wouldn't have made any difference. It seems that his views on divorce, which would in any case have debarred him from marrying me, are resolute and unalterable. Max hinted at that some time ago. But I—could never have become his wife. I think in the end I—I almost came to hate him.' By now, her voice was scarcely audible. 'This weekend, while you were away,

185

I decided to bring my engagement to an end. He simply got in first. So now you know it all.'

He came to stand by her side, lifted her left hand, saw the ring had gone, noted her bare wrist. 'So he's taken the lot.' He flicked through the forms she had filled in. 'What do you think you're going to do with these?'

'I went to the secretarial agency this afternoon. I've got to get some sort of job because I need the money. They're going to find me a temporary one. I intend eventually to get one overseas, provided of course that you allow me to give your name when they require a reference.' Her voice faltered. 'Provided, also, you give me a good one. They're very particular about references for jobs abroad.'

'So you think I should give you a good reference? Suppose I don't?'

She lifted her shoulders. 'In that case, I couldn't get a job, could I?' She raised desolate eyes to his, and his expression puzzled her.

After a moment, he spoke again. 'So you're intending to put as many miles between us as possible?'

'Why not? As you said about yourself this morning, I'm a free agent now. I can do what I like, go where I like and when I like. I'm on my own.' Her voice broke and her hand groped downwards to the dog at her side. 'So I should be obliged if you would, from now on, regard yourself simply as a tenant, and not as my keeper, m-my husband, boy-friend, boss or—or anything else you can think of.'

She knelt beside the dog and hid her face against him, crying softly into his fur. He didn't move, just lay there giving her comfort, which in his own animal way he seemed to know she needed.

Jon's words were quiet when they came. 'Is it a habit of yours to put thousands of miles between yourself and the man you love?'

'What does it matter?' Her voice was muffled. 'The man I love doesn't love me.'

Jon crouched down beside her. 'How do you know?' He was whispering now. 'Have you asked him?'

She didn't move.

'Ask him, Kathy. Ask him now.'

But she was silent.

'Ask him if he's madly in love with you. Ask him if he can be in the same room as you without wanting desperately to take you in his arms and never release you.'

Still she did not move. He stood up.

'Kathy,' his voice was urgent, 'if you don't stop clinging to my dog as though he were a life-raft in a raging sea and come to me of your own accord, I shall have to prise you away from him—and that, my darling, might hurt the dog.'

A great sob was torn from her and she rose and turned blindly in his direction and clung to him with all her strength.

'Jon, oh, Jon,' she whispered, and hid her face against him. He held her as if he would never let her go. She looked into his eyes, and saw in them the depth of his love for her.

'Jon.' Her voice held a note of wonder. 'You've come back. After all these years, you've come back.'

'Yes, my darling wife, I've come back. And this time I've come to stay.'

He led her to the couch and pulled her down into his arms. They sat, quiet and contented, until Jon began to talk.

'You must surely want to know, my darling, why I spoke to you as I did this morning. I had no alternative. I'd spent a weekend of unbelievable misery with my sister's family, talking about you, thinking about you, loving you, wanting you. Those few days we spent together at the conference were like a tantalising glimpse of Paradise. When we parted at the station, I thought it was Paradise lost. I came home early from my sister's house because I couldn't bear to be away from you. Yet, when I returned to my office this morning and saw you there, and felt you so close to me, knowing you were for ever, as I thought, out of my reach, I realised I couldn't stand it any longer. One of us had to go and I knew it would have to be you. I had to drive you away from me or go mad. Do you understand and forgive me?'

'Jon, the times you've torn my heart out. That letter . . .' He interrupted her question.

'That letter, sweetheart, is safely in my wallet. Did you really think I would do such a thing to something so precious to me that I preserved it all those years?'

'Why did you pretend, Jon?'

'Why did I pretend? she asks me. What have I been trying to do all these weeks but provoke you into giving away your feel-

187

ings about me? Geoff told me he thought you were still in love with me——'

'He did? When?'

'That night you went to your first rehearsal. I met you at the bathroom door, remember?' They smiled at the memory. 'I didn't see how Geoff could be right, and even when I tried to prove to myself he was right because I wanted him to be, you wouldn't give in. Almost from the start I did everything I could think of to break through your defences, but your self-control was incredible. I tried making love to you, I kissed you. I tried making you jealous, I even tried insulting you to get you to cry in my arms, but you wouldn't even cry on my shoulder. You chose, instead, to do it in the arms of my deadliest rival. Or so I regarded him at the time.'

'Why did you hate Max so?'

'Couldn't you recognise stark, excruciating jealousy when you saw it? I recognised early that he was in love with you. I was sure you loved him in return. The night of the party I convinced myself I had lost the battle and I lost control.' He tilted her face to his. 'I owe you a profound apology for the way I treated you in Annette's bedroom.'

'But, Jon, that was the night I returned to life. I knew I was back where I belonged—in your arms. My feelings seemed to free themselves from the strait-jacket I had imprisoned them in since you left me all those years ago.'

'Each time I kissed you, I felt that the ice melted a little. Is that true?' She nodded. 'So my ice-maiden came to life before my eyes.' His lips pressed against her hair. 'You know, you were an enigma. At times you seemed so innocent, yet at other times you seemed to be up to your eyes in intrigue. Scientist that I am, I began to observe and analyse every situation as it arose. I shut up my heart and tried to judge you dispassionately—very difficult indeed, my beloved, when the person concerned is someone you love—but I knew that was the only way I could arrive at the truth.'

'Jon,' she played with his tie, 'there never was another man. I made him up.'

'Sweetheart, I know that now. You told me yourself so many times and in so many ways, without even realising it.' He dropped a kiss on her forehead. 'Max—came to see me, Kathy, the day after the party, when you were nursing his father. He

188

swore to me that there was nothing between you. He told me how you had cried in the car,' his voice softened, 'and that he loved you, but you didn't return his love. He told me then, cryptically, that your heart was locked up and he envied with all his soul the man who held the key.'

They were silent for a while, then she turned in his arms and looked earnestly into his eyes. 'Jon, what about Annette?'

'Annette? She, my sweet one, is not all she hopes she seems to be.'

'But her reputation, Jon?'

'Oh, like so many people with so-called reputations, it's nearly all myth, carefully nurtured to give others the impression that she leads an eventful private life. People like her build up these "reputations" to mask their shortcomings with the opposite sex. After all, to put it crudely, Annette hasn't yet caught her man, has she?' He saw the anxiety which still hovered in her eyes. 'I can see you'll be satisfied with nothing less than a full confession. Well, you're not going to get that, my sweet. I haven't been perfect in the intervening years, but neither have I been the unprincipled rake you seem to think I was. I had girl-friends, yes, they came and went, but I never got seriously involved. Otherwise, they would have "come", but they would never have "went", would they?' He smiled. 'See what I mean?'

She nodded.

'Kathy,' he whispered, 'let me tell you a secret. I'm not carved out of stone as you once said I was. I have a heart, and it's beating, sweetheart, beating hard and fast. Feel it.' He took her hand and pressed it to him. She could feel the strong rapid throb beneath her fingers. 'Blood flows in my veins, swift and strong. And warm. Beloved, let me show you how warm.'

He crushed her to him, his lips sought hers, found them and clung to them, and they were lost to the world.

Geoff let himself in the front door. 'Kath?' he called. 'What happened to you today?' He looked into her living-room.

'Oh, sorry,' he said. Then he stopped, looked again at the two figures so close together on the couch. They did not stir. Geoff dropped his briefcase and put a hand to his head.

'Sorry? Did I say I was sorry? What on earth am I talking about? This is the best thing that's happened in years. Hey, Flop, come with me. We're going to phone Helen to tell her the good news, then we're going out—to buy some champagne. Come on, boy. Have we got something to celebrate!'

The dog heard the whistle and raced out of the room. His tail, which he flourished madly from side to side, caught the edge of the door as he flashed past. It swung slowly shut behind him.

Take these 4 best-selling novels FREE